UNDER START__ _ ORDERS

HORSE RACING QUIZ BOOK

Written by Chris Coley and Steve Jones

All proceeds from the sale of this book will go to the Injured Jockeys Fund.

The Injured Jockeys Fund helps any rider who holds, or has held, a Professional or Amateur licence issued by the British Horse Racing Authority including Apprentice, Conditional and Point-to-Point riders, including any spouse, partner, child or dependant they may have. They have a team of eight Almoners offering help and support nationwide, and through the Charity's three Rehabilitation and Fitness Centres.

Copyright © Chris Coley and Steve Jones 2021.
Production - Charlie Pritchard LPD – 01295 680956
ISBN 978-1-3999-0394-3
A catalogue record for this book is available from the British Library.

FOREWORD

EVERY jockey goes to the races hoping they will ride a winner. The reality, especially for those riding over jumps, is that it's nearly as likely they will end up on the turf rather than in the winners' enclosure.

Falls are an occupational hazard for every rider and that's why the Injured Jockeys Fund is so invaluable.

Since it was founded in 1964, the help it has given to riders, both past and present, has increased year by year. Thanks to the tireless work of its trustees, staff, presidents, patrons and fundraisers, the safety net it offers jockeys is now wider and more comprehensive than it has ever been.

The Fund runs three world-class rehab and fitness centres. Oaksey House in Lambourn, Jack Berry House in Malton and Peter O'Sullevan House in Newmarket have made a huge difference to jockeys' wellbeing.

They are very humbling places and I don't know how racing ever managed without them. Not only do they help with rehabilitation, as well as the care of those with long-term injuries, they are also crucial to helping prevent injuries.

It's always great to see so many jockeys of all codes in the centres keeping themselves fit and healthy. Prevention is better than cure and the fitter you can be minimises the chance of getting injured.

These centres alone cost more than £2million to run each year and they are just one part of the wide-ranging support offered by the Injured Jockeys Fund.

Fortunately, racing is very good at looking after its own and we're lucky the charity has so many generous supporters. In total, we need to raise more than £4million every year to fund all the crucial work.

The majority comes from donations and third-party fundraising like this hugely-enjoyable quiz book.

I've had a good flick through and I'm pleased to say I did know a few of the answers. Most of them were from 20 years ago - I can remember much more about those days than I can about what happened last month!

I've even set a round of questions myself along with more than 20 other racing personalities including Frankie Dettori, Paul Nicholls, Richard Johnson John Francome and many more.

All the rounds are really interesting, informative and great fun and many have a theme which should give you a clue to some of the answers... and I'm sure the questions will tax the brainpower of the keenest racing fan!

I hope this book gives you many hours of pleasure and, remember, you're supporting a cause that's crucial to the sport of horseracing.

Your support is greatly appreciated.

Sir AP McCoy OBE
President, Injured Jockeys Fund

CONTENTS

ROUND	TITLE	PAGE

ROUND	TITLE	PAGE

ROUND 1
AP McCOY

1 I won the conditional jockeys' championship in 1995 – my first full season in England – when I was attached to which trainer?

2 I rode my first winner on Legal Steps in a Flat race at Thurles for which trainer?

3 In 2002, I beat the long-standing record, set in 1947, of which Flat jockey for the most winners ridden in a single season in Britain? The record stood at 269 and I ended the campaign with 289 winners.

4 When I rode Mighty Montefalco to victory at Uttoxeter, whose all-time record of jumps winners did I beat?

5 On which horse did I finish third in the Grand National in both 2001 and 2002?

6 On which horse did I win the Cheltenham Gold Cup before he was tragically killed in the Grand National just a few weeks later?

7 Which football team do I support?

8 I was involved in the naming of the horse 'The Romford Pele'. He was named after which ex-footballer and friend of mine?

9 Which horse did Martin Pipe tell me was "the biggest certainty that will ever walk out onto this racecourse" as we left the parade ring at the 1998 Cheltenham Festival before winning what is now the Pertemps Final?

10 Which horse gave me the first of my three Champion Hurdle wins?

ROUND 2
CORNELIUS LYSAGHT

1 I grew up in Herefordshire just down the road from a champion jump jockey who might be said to have won the title seven-and-a-half times having shared it in the 1981/82 season. Who is he?

2 It was also near to where a successful jumps trainer grew up. His first 'rules' winner, ridden by him as well, was Last Of The Foxes at our local track in February 1981. Who is he?

3 I was sent to school at Eton where I was in classes alongside the trainer of two Hennessy Gold Cup winners of the 1990s. He also rode the winner of the Cheltenham Festival Hunter Chase on Observe. Who is he?

4 Another of my contemporaries was a jump jockey who won the 33rd Whitbread Gold Cup at Sandown in 1989 on Brown Windsor. Who is he?

5 Another school friend and now pressroom colleague was Aintree Grand National-winning rider Marcus Armytage. His trainer-dad Roddy won the Scottish National twice in the 1970s with which horse?

6 When I joined the BBC Radio in 1990, who was racing correspondent and commentator, a role in which he continued until 2001?

7 The answer to number 6 coined the phrase "you need a telescope to see the rest" when which horse won the 1981 Derby?

8 My ex-BBC colleague John Inverdale was part-owner of a Flat horse that they sold before he won the Champion Hurdle as Martin Pipe's second winner of the race. What was the horse called?

9 Another colleague, Ian Robertson, had a number of horses, mainly trained by Ian Balding, including one called Twickenham. What was his specialist sport at the BBC?

10 I gave Ian Balding's daughter Clare her first broadcasting job after she left university where she was President of the Union. Which university?

ROUND 3
PAUL NICHOLLS

1   On which horse did I win the Hennessy Gold Cup and the Welsh National as a jockey in 1987?

2   With whom did I serve a two-year apprenticeship as a trainer?

3   Which horse won the Grand National for that stable when I was assistant trainer?

4   My big breakthrough as a trainer came when Call Equiname won the Champion Chase, Flagship Uberalles landed the Arkle and See More Business lifted the Gold Cup. What was the year?

5   The previous year See More Business had been carried out in the Gold Cup by which horse ridden by Tony McCoy?

6   Which horse, that I trained, was controversially remounted to finish a short-head second behind Mistral De La Cour in a novices' chase at Exeter in 2004?

7   At which racecourse in 2006 did I saddle six winners on the same card?

8   Which jockey took the wrong course on 2-5 favourite Oumeyade, trained by me, in the Prince of Wales Cup at Fakenham in 2008?

9   As of 2021, I had trained 46 winners at the Cheltenham Festival. Which race have I won six times?

10   Which jockey twice missed out on a Grand National ride for me having suffered injuries in serious falls from both Celestial Halo and Zarkandar in the Aintree Hurdle shortly before the big race?

ROUND 4
CLARE BALDING

1   I presented racing on the BBC for 15 years with which Classic-winning and champion jockey as my sidekick?

2   Our last broadcast together was on Champions Day at Ascot in 2012 when which horse completed his unbeaten career with victory in the Champion Stakes?

3   When my brother Andrew won the Oaks in 2003 in his very first season as a trainer, I couldn't interview him properly because we were all crying. What was the name of the filly and who rode her?

4   When I rode as an amateur jockey, I won the Ladies' Championship in 1990. As a prize I won my weight in what?

5   I am one of the presenters for the BBC Sports Personality of the Year. Who is the only jockey to have won SPOTY?

6   Two other jockeys have also finished in the top three in the public vote. Who are they?

7   Over the last 25 years, the record audience for the Grand National was on the BBC in 1997 when more than 15.1 million people tuned in on a Monday evening for the race that had been rescheduled because of a bomb scare. Which horse won?

8   I have written three novels for children about a racehorse called Noble Warrior. What was the first book called?

9   In 2013, I presented a documentary on Channel 4 to mark the centenary of the so-called 'Suffragette Derby'. What was the name of the Suffragette who died from her injuries and what was the name of the horse she brought down?

10 Complete the title of my latest book for children: Fall Off....

ROUND 5
GREEN FINGERS

All the questions relate to gardens and horticulture

1 Which track is known as Yorkshire's garden racecourse?

2 Which celebrated garden designer of the 18th century gave his name to the winner of the 1993 Reynoldstown Novices' Chase, trained by Martin Pipe?

3 Which triple Group 1 winner, including the 2018 Lockinge Stakes, was named after the largest genus of the Ericaceae family and the national flower of Nepal? These shrubs can be found growing next to the walk from the parade ring to the track at Sandown.

4 The winner of which race is adorned with a blanket of 554 red roses in the winners' enclosure? The presentation has led to the race being nicknamed the 'run for the roses'.

5 The Old Roan Chase, run at Aintree in October, now carries the name of which three-times winner of the race?

6 Which French-trained horse, winner of the 2000 Triumph Hurdle, was named after a white flower grown from a bulb and often seen in woodlands in early spring?

7 Kew Gardens led home a one-two-three for Aidan O'Brien in which race at Royal Ascot in 2018?

8 Which garden implement did Vincent O'Brien train to win three successive Cheltenham Gold Cups?

9 Which horse, named after a hardy twining climber that's often colourful and fragrant, won the Irish Champion Hurdle in 2020 and 2021?

10 Which horse, trained by Jonjo O'Neill, won the Stayers' Hurdle and Liverpool Hurdle in 2004?

ROUND 6
MASKED JOCKEYS

Identify the flat jockeys in their Covid masks

ROUND 7
KEEP IT IN THE FAMILY

All the question relate to brothers and sisters

1   Which brothers both rode Larbawn to win the Whitbread Gold Cup at Sandown? The wins came in successive years.

2   Which brothers both rode Cheltenham Gold Cup winners in the 1950s?

3   Which brothers, born in Puerto Rico, both won the American Eclipse Award for outstanding jockey in recent years?

4   Bullet Train acted as pacemaker for his illustrious younger brother on six occasions. What was his name?

5   Which full-brothers won a Champion Hurdle each in the 1990s?

6   Which female jockey rode three Cheltenham Festival winners, while her brother partnered 59 winners at jump racing's biggest meeting?

7   Which champion Flat jockey has two brothers who are successful jump jockeys and a sister who is a TV presenter?

8   With 5,425 winners between them, who are the most prolific jockey brothers in British racing history?

9   Silverburn won two Grade 1 races in the 2000s – the Tolworth Novices' Hurdle and the Scilly Isles Novices' Chase, both at Sandown. Who was his more illustrious full-brother?

10   Which twin brothers rode the winners of every Classic between them. One of them won the 1000 Guineas, 2000 Guineas, Oaks and St Leger. The other landed the Derby?

ROUND 8
SEEING IS BELIEVING

All these questions and answers are connected to rather surprising events and accomplishments

1 Which horse won a race on both the first and last days of Royal Ascot in both 1962 and 1963?

2 Morley Street and Alderbrook both won at Glorious Goodwood before winning which race the following year?

3 Who owned Mandarin, the first winner of the Hennessy Gold Cup?

4 Who trained Life Of A Lord to win the Whitbread Gold Cup in 1996?

5 Sir Gordon Richards won the Derby on Pinza at the 26th attempt just weeks after receiving his knighthood. Who owned the runner-up Aureole?

6 Which jockey rode the winners of the Cheltenham Gold Cup, Champion Hurdle and the Grand National as well as finishing runner-up in the Derby?

7 The first female jockey to win a British Group 1 Flat race was Alex Greaves when she partnered Ya Malak in the 1997 Nunthorpe Stakes at York. Why was the win unusual?

8 Stoney Crossing came third at 100-1 behind which two horses in the Cheltenham Gold Cup before coming sixth at the Badminton Horse Trials the following month?

9 Which horse won nine handicaps in a season in both 1985 and 1988?

10 What was notable about Royal Wedding's win at Fontwell on 29 April 2011?

ROUND 9
CULTURE VULTURES

All the questions relate to arts and literature

1   Which horse, named after the hero of a series of short stories penned by Sir Arthur Conan Doyle, suffered his only defeat in 18 races when runner-up in what is now the Juddmonte International Stakes at York in the first year the race was run?

2   Nijinsky, who famously won the Triple Crown in 1970, was named after the Polish ballet dancer by his owner's wife. Who was his owner?

3   Nigel Twiston-Davies won the 1998 Punchestown Gold Cup with a horse named after a composer whose music was banned by the Nazis. What was the horse called?

4   Which horse gave Aidan O'Brien his first win in the Arc de Triomphe? He was named after a poet and writer whose most famous work was a play set in the fictional town of Llareggub.

5   Pat Eddery's last ride in the Derby, who was named after a book by American writer F Scott Fitzgerald, finished runner-up behind Kris Kin. What was the horse called?

6   Which horse, named after a Shakespeare play, was ridden to his two Champion Hurdle wins by Bill Smith and Ken White?

7   Which horse, owned by actor James Nesbitt, won the Ryanair Chase at the 2012 Cheltenham Festival? His name is a pointer to his owner's profession.

8   Which horse, trained by his father, gave Joseph O'Brien his first Classic winner when he won the 2011 Irish 2,000 Guineas? He was named after an Irish painter.

9   Which horse, named after an influential French composer, won the 2010 Arlington Million for John Gosden and William Buick?

10   Which horse was Vincent O'Brien's sixth and final Derby winner? His name was taken from a symbol of authority and kingship in Greek mythology.

ROUND 10
RED RUM'S THIRD GRAND NATIONAL VICTORY

All the questions relate to Red Rum's Grand National exploits

1 Ginger McCain famously trained Red Rum on the beach of which seaside town?

2 When Red Rum won his third Grand National the runner-up had won the Topham Trophy over the big Aintree fences just two days earlier. What was the horse?

3 Tommy Stack rode Red Rum when he won his third Grand National after Brian Fletcher had been in the saddle for his first two wins. What was the name of Fletcher's other Grand National winner?

4 As well as winning three Grand Nationals, Red Rum also twice finished runner-up in the great Aintree race. Which Cheltenham Gold Cup winner beat him in 1975?

5 The 1977 Grand National was also notable for the first female jockey to ride in the race. Riding her horse Barony Fort, a 200-1 shot, they refused four fences from home. Who was the rider?

6 Which famous comedian, actor and panel show regular worked as a stable lad for Ginger McCain? The first horse he sat on was Red Rum.

ROUND 11
THE FEMALE
OF THE SPECIES

All the questions relate to fillies and mares

1. The Grade 1 Mares' Hurdle held on the opening day of the Cheltenham Festival is run in memory of which champion jumps trainer?

2. In days gone by the three-legged mare had crowds flocking to the Knavesmire, now home to York Racecourse. What was it?

3. Which mare is the only horse to have won both the Champion Hurdle and the Cheltenham Gold Cup?

4. Which horse was the last to win the fillies' Triple Crown?

5. Which Classic trial for fillies is named after a long-time mistress of King Charles II?

6. Which filly in 2020 completed the 1000 Guineas and Oaks double?

7. The Falmouth Stakes at Newmarket's July Meeting was upgraded to Group 1 status in 2004. Who was the winner?

8. In 1992, Marling won the Irish 1,000 Guineas, Coronation Stakes and Sussex Stakes. She had earlier been beaten a head in the 1000 Guineas when enduring a troubled run. Who beat her in the Newmarket Classic?

9. User Friendly won her first six races including the Oaks, Irish Oaks and St Leger before finishing runner-up in the Arc de Triomphe. Who rode her in all her races in Britain?

10. A total of 13 mares have won the Grand National. The last of those came in 1951. Who was she?

ROUND 12
COLOUR CODED

All the answers contain a colour

1   Which horse gave Gordon Elliott his first Grand National victory?

2   Which horse, trained by Donald McCain, won the first David Nicholson Mare's Hurdle when it was introduced to the Cheltenham Festival in 2008?

3   Which winner of the Golden Jubilee Stakes became the first horse from outside of Europe to be named Champion Sprinter at the Cartier Awards in 2012?

4   Which horse, owned by Lord Rosebery, won both the 2000 Guineas and Derby in 1939 but was prevented from attempting to win The Triple Crown when the St Leger was cancelled due to the outbreak of WWII?

5   Which mare won the 2007 Lockinge Stakes and is the mother of Arc de Triomphe winner Found?

6   Which horse gave disgraced Godolphin trainer Mahmood Al Zarooni his first British Classic win when landing the 1000 Guineas in 2011?

7   Which horse, officially recorded as being white in colour, won the 2016 Classic Chase at Warwick?

8   Which well-known owner's best horses included Carvill's Hill and Champion Hurdler winner Hors La Loi?

9   Which colour links the two 150-1 shots that filled the places behind Commander In Chief in the 1993 Derby?

10 Jockey James Doyle and trainer Michael Bell teamed up to win the Gold Cup at Royal Ascot in 2017 with which horse?

ROUND 13
DRINKS CABINET

All the questions relate to drinks

1 Trainer Ryan Price won what is now the Betfair Hurdle four times in five years during the 1960s. What was the race, run at Newbury, known as in those days?

2 Which horse, bearing the name of an Australian wine district, won the Hennessy Gold Cup (now the Ladbrokes Trophy) in 2007 and 2009 and also won the Cheltenham Gold Cup?

3 Which Canadian distillery corporation sponsored the Grand National from 1984 to 1991? In the final year of its sponsorship a horse by the same name won the great Aintree race.

4 Which horse won seven consecutive hurdle races in the mid-1970s, including an undefeated season when he won the English, Welsh and Scottish Champion Hurdles?

5 Which iconic Irish drink has its own 'village' at the Cheltenham Festival?

6 Which course hosts the Champagne Stakes, a seven-furlong Group 2 race for two-year-olds?

7 Which horse, with a drink contained in his name, won the 1972 Cesarewitch? He was named after a famous coming-of-age book chronicling the author's childhood growing up in the Cotswolds.

8 Who was the original sponsor of the 2m4f handicap chase run at Cheltenham in November? It has since been sponsored by Murphy's, Thomas Pink, BetVictor and Paddy Power.

9 The Irish Derby was sponsored by which brand of beer from 1986 to 2007?

10 Which horse, named after a cocktail made with the national spirit of Peru combined with lime, syrup and egg white, won the 2011 Hampton Court Stakes at Royal Ascot for Hughie Morrison?

ROUND 14
LANDED GENTRY

All the questions relate to Lords, Ladies, Sirs, Dames and other titles

1   TV betting pundit John McCririck used to refer to one of his Channel 4 colleagues as 'The Noble Lord'. Who was he?

2   Which horse gave Martin Dwyer victory in the Derby when narrowly landing the Epsom Classic in 2006?

3   Sir Rembrandt finished runner-up in the Cheltenham Gold Cup behind which horse?

4   Which prominent owner/breeder was chairman of Cheltenham Racecourse from 1990 to 2011?

5   Jim Culloty famously partnered Best Mate to three Cheltenham Gold Cup victories but which horse did he train to win the Festival feature in 2014?

6   Who owns the Goodwood Estate in Sussex where the racecourse is situated?

7   Who trained Sir Harry Lewis to win the 1987 Irish Derby?

8   Which horse gave Nigel Twiston-Davies his first and, as of 2021, only win in the Midlands Grand National?

9   For what was Sir Michael Stoute made a Knight Bachelor in 1998?

10   Who owned top filly Ouija Board? Having won the Oaks and Irish Oaks in 2004 she went on to land five more Group/Grade 1 contests including races at two Breeders Cup meetings.

All the questions relate to the events of 2021

1 Which 13-year-old, who once beat Bristol De Mai in a match race at Carlisle, landed the final of the Veterans' Chase Series at Sandown on the first weekend in January?

2 When Gordon Elliott was banned from training for 12 months (six months suspended), which trainer took temporary charge of the stables?

3 How many British-trained hurdles winners were there at the Cheltenham Festival?

4 On which horse did Rachael Blackmore became the first female jockey to win the Grand National?

5 Which Derby runner was Adam Kirby 'jocked off' by Frankie Dettori before picking up the ride on eventual winner Adayar?

6 Which horse gave Aidan O'Brien his first success in the Prix du Jockey Club (French Derby)?

7 Euchen Glen caused a 20-1 shock in the Group 3 Brigadier Gerard Stakes at Sandown in May. Who trains him?

8 Which jockey was the leading rider at Royal Ascot with five winners?

9 Which apprentice jockey rode Real World, trained by Saeed bin Suroor, to win the Royal Hunt Cup?

10 Which high-profile sporting promoter's wife Susan bred Subjectivist, winner of the Gold Cup at Royal Ascot?

ROUND 16
LAND OF MY FATHERS

All the questions relate to Wales

1   Which company has sponsored the Welsh National since 1973, making it the longest running sponsorship in jump racing?

2   Since WWII, which Welsh jockey has ridden two Grand National winners?

3   Which racecourse became the first new National Hunt track for 80 years when it opened its doors in 2009?

4   What is the name of the trotting club that hosts the biggest annual festival of harness racing in the UK?

5   Which Welsh jockey rode Mill Reef to win the 1971 Derby and Arc de Triomphe?

6   Which Pembrokeshire-based trainer won three successive Topham Chases over Aintree's Grand National fences with Always Waining?

7   Chepstow trainer Milton Bradley won the King's Stand Stakes at Royal Ascot in 2004 with which popular sprinter?

8   What was the name of the Carmarthen dairy farmer who both owned and trained Norton's Coin to win the 1990 Cheltenham Gold Cup at 100-1?

9   Which horse, named after a Welsh county, finished runner-up in successive Arc de Triomphes behind Treve and Golden Horn?

10 Which Henry Cecil-trained horse, named after a town in Wales, started odds-on favourite for the 1993 Derby but could only finish tenth behind stablemate Commander In Chief?

MATCH THE NAME

Match the horses with the picture of the landmark, fictional character or famous person that they were named after

1 Went off favourite for the 1977 Grand National and was ten lengths clear when falling at Becher's Brook second time round in the race best remembered for Red Rum's third win in the great race. This horse went on to win the Whitbread Gold Cup a few weeks later.

2 Given the nickname of the 'Iron Horse' after winning the St James's Palace Stakes, Eclipse Stakes, Sussex Stakes, Juddmonte International and Irish Champion Stakes in 2000. He didn't finish out of the first two in all 14 of his career races, including when runner-up in the Breeders' Cup Classic.

3 Cheltenham Gold Cup winner in 1987 when the race was delayed by more than an hour due to heavy snow. His trainer wasn't even at the track having chosen to saddle runners closer to home at Hexham. This horse also won the Midlands National and the Tommy Whittle Chase.

4 European Champion Three-Year-Old Colt in 2012 having won the 2000 Guineas, Derby and Irish Derby. He was denied the British Triple Crown when controversially finishing runner-up in the St Leger.

5 Finished fourth behind Sea The Stars in the 2000 Guineas and Derby before landing the Sussex Stakes and Queen Elizabeth II Stakes in 2009. Stayed in training the following year when he added the Juddmonte International to his big-race haul.

6 Trained in Ireland by Mick Rogers to win the Irish 2,000 Guineas, Derby and Irish Derby in 1964 before finishing runner-up in the Arc de Triomphe. Irish St Leger winner Reindeer was among his best offspring.

7 Dual winner of the Maryland Cup before this American-owned crossed the Atlantic to join trainer Tim Forster and land the 1980 Grand National. He was ridden by American amateur jockey and merchant banker Charlie Fenwick at Aintree.

8 Son of super stallion Galileo, who won the 2018 Derby when his trainer had five of the first six home in the Epsom Classic. His only subsequent victory came when beating Stradivarius in the Prix Foy at Longchamp on Arc trials day the following year.

ROUND 18
THE LONG AND THE SHORT OF IT

All the questions relate to measurements

1 How many furlongs make up a mile?

2 What is smallest possible winning distance in the UK?

3 At 5ft 3ins what is the tallest fence on the Grand National course?

4 Which course, at approximately two miles, is the longest round Flat racing circuit in Britain?

5 Which British racecourse has the smallest circumference being just 1m1f round?

6 Horses are measured by 'hands' in the UK. How many inches in one hand?

7 How many miles by road is it from Perth, the course furthest north in the UK, to Newton Abbot, the track furthest south?

8 How tall was Lester Piggott when he was riding?

9 What is the highest Flat racecourse in Britain?

10 According to the Guinness Book Of Records, the fastest five-furlong race was completed by Stone Of Folca in a time of 53.69 seconds in 2012. At which course was the race run?

ROUND 19
AROUND THE TRACKS

All the answers are British or Irish racecourses

1   Which racecourse has the longest run-in from the last fence to the winning post?

2   Household management author Mrs Beeton lived in a flat with her step-father who was clerk of the course at which track?

3   Which racecourse is located at Piercefield Park?

4   Which Irish racecourse is often referred to as Ballybrit, due to its exact location near the city of the track's usual name?

5   Which racecourse is situated on the Scone Palace estate?

6   Which racecourse has a golf course in the middle and is crossed at three intersections by the B4365 road on non-racedays?

7   At which course did Pope John Paul II address a crowd of 190,000 on marriage and family life?

8   Part of which course runs alongside the River Dove?

9   Which racecourse is comprised of two separate tracks that are stretched out over two separate counties?

10 Which British racecourse is situated nearest to a cathedral?

ROUND 20
CLOSE BUT NO CIGAR

All the questions relate to runners-up

1 Which horse, who raced since the turn of the Millennium, finished second in the Triumph Hurdle, Paddy Power Gold Cup, Caspian Caviar Gold Cup and Topham Chase?

2 Pearlyman notched the second of his Queen Mother Champion Chase victories in 1988. Who finished second?

3 Best Mate famously won three Cheltenham Gold Cups. He finished runner-up in the Supreme Novices' Hurdle on his only other appearance at the Cheltenham Festival. Who beat him?

4 Which horse finished runner-up behind Frankel on four occasions, including in three Group 1s?

5 How many times was Richard Johnson runner-up behind AP McCoy in the race to be champion jump jockey?

6 Which Cheltenham Gold Cup-winning jockey finished second when Lester Piggott rode his first winner on The Chase at Haydock in 1948?

7 Shergar famously won the Derby by a record ten lengths in 1981. Who finished second?

8 Who rode Dancing Brave when he was controversially beaten by Shahrastani in the 1986 Derby?

9 In the summer of 2019, Stradivarius completed the notable hat-trick of Royal Ascot's Gold Cup, the Goodwood Cup and the Lonsdale Cup at York. Who finished second in all three races?

10 Aidan O'Brien trained his second 2000 Guineas winner when Rock Of Gibraltar, part owned by Sir Alex Ferguson, was successful in 2002. Which stablemate finished second?

ROUND 21
MONEY MATTERS

All the questions relate to money and sponsorship

1   The 1000 Guineas and 2000 Guineas are the first two Classics of the Flat season. How much would their monetary titles be worth combined in modern currency?

2   The Saudi Cup, the most valuable race in the world worth $20million, took place in February 2021 but which city staged the race?

3   The bet365 Gold Cup is run on the last day of the jumps season at Sandown. Which brewing company was the original sponsor, backing the race from 1957 until 2001?

4   Which company has sponsored British Champions Day since its inception in 2011?

5   Which company was the first to sponsor the Derby when backing the Epsom classic in 1984?

6   Which American rider, christened Brian Keith before legally changing his name to a money-related moniker, rode more than 3,000 winners? He retired in 2001.

7   Which big-spending jumps owner won £550,000 from William Hill when Frankie Dettori rode all seven winners at Ascot in 1996? He paid a National Hunt record £620,000 for Interconnected in 2019.

8   Which drinks brand sponsored the Cheltenham Gold Cup in 2019 and 2020?

9   How much did it cost to supplement a horse into the 2021 Derby?

10   Which newspaper sponsored the first running of the Festival Trophy in 2005? The race has since become known as the Ryanair Chase and is run on the Thursday of the Cheltenham Festival.

ROUND 22
FAMILY CONNECTIONS

On the left-hand page there are photos of a father who has a son or daughter on the right-hand page. Match up the father with their offspring

Photos courtesy of focusonracing.com and Bernard Parkin

ROUND 23
FRANKIE DETTORI

1   When my father Gianfranco won the 2000 Guineas on Bolkonski in 1975 it was which trainer's first Classic winner?

2   Which horse gave me my first British Classic victory when landing the 1994 Oaks?

3   At the start of the 2021 season there was just one British Group 1 race that I hadn't won. Which race?

4   When I first came to Britain I was apprenticed and then stable jockey to which trainer?

5   Which British football team do I support?

6   When I rode my 'Magnificent Seven' winners at Ascot on Queen Elizabeth II Stakes day in 1996 which horse did I ride to win the day's big race?

7   I've won the Dubai World Cup three times. Which horse, with a particularly appropriate name, gave me my first victory in the race when successful in 2000?

8   When I was a team captain on the TV show Question Of Sport, which footballer captained the opposing side?

9   How many Group 1 races did I win on dual Arc de Triomphe winner Enable?

10   I've won the Gold Cup at Royal Ascot eight times. Which horse has been responsible for three of them?

ROUND 24
NICK LUCK

1   My earliest childhood racing memories are of point-to-pointing at Tweseldown near Fleet in Hampshire. Why did the racecourse make history in the mid-1990s?

2   I was born in Heatherwood Hospital next to Ascot Racecourse. A couple of weeks earlier Sir Michael Stoute had won the Gold Cup at Royal Ascot with which horse?

3   My family lived next to the defunct racecourse at Hawthorn Hill, near Maidenhead. It was later turned into a golf course by which high-profile racehorse owner?

4   My first visit to Fontwell Park was in May 1988. Which horse, that I saw that day, went on to win eight races at the Sussex track?

5   My godfather Josh Gifford took 18 years as a trainer to break his duck at the Cheltenham Festival before winning the Kim Muir Chase with Golden Minstrel. Which amateur jockey rode him?

6   I missed watching Lammtarra's Derby because I was stuck in an A-Level Theatre Studies workshop singing 'Papa's got a head like a Ping Pong Ball' to the tune of the William Tell Overture. I had backed Presenting, who finished third for John Gosden, but which international jockey rode him?

7   In 1996 I spent a year as an intern at Kentucky Equine Research. Which Essex-born trainer saddled nine straight winners at the Churchill Downs spring meet and finished up winning 14 races from 17 runners?

8   I first went to the Derby in 1999, the year Oath won. At which track did he win his first race? Recent Derby winners Golden Horn and Adayar also broke their maidens at this course.

9   The first Cheltenham Festival I covered for Racing UK (now Racing TV) was in 2005. Who were the leading trainer and jockey who teamed up for three wins taking both novice hurdles and the Stayers' Hurdle?

10   In November 2006, I covered the Tattersalls Breeding Stock sale where the sale topper was Magical Romance, in-foal to Pivotal, who cost £4.83million. Why did this look very expensive only a month later?

ROUND 25
JOHN FRANCOME

1 What was the name of my first winner?

2 Who was the famous BBC sports commentator whose daughter was in the British junior showjumping team with me?

3 Who was the former jockey who was my partner in our fish & chip business?

4 I finished second in the Colonial Cup in America on a former Champion Hurdler. What was his name?

5 When I was stable jockey to Fred Winter at his Uplands stables in Lambourn which trainer, who trained for the Queen Mother, was based next door at Saxon House Stables?

6 Who was the Spanish aristocrat amateur jockey who realised a lifelong ambition when riding his own Nereo, trained by Fred Winter, to finish eighth in the 1973 Grand National? It was the first time he completed the course at the sixth attempt.

7 What was unusual about my win on Midnight Court in the 1978 Cheltenham Gold Cup?

8 Fred Winter is still the only man to win which three big jumps races as a jockey and as a trainer?

9 I won 17 races on a lovely horse called Osbaldeston. What was the name of his full brother who won a race at the grand old age of 18?

10 I won the Welsh National, Hennessy Gold Cup and King George VI Chase on Burrough Hill Lad but I didn't ride him when he won the Cheltenham Gold Cup. Who did?

ROUND 26
BROUGH SCOTT

1 What was the name of the famous horse my grandfather bred and rode in France throughout WWI, cheating death many times? When he died in 1941 The Times ran an obituary with the headline 'The Horse The Germans Couldn't Kill'. I republished my grandfather's book about his exploits.

2 What is my real first name?

3 Which famous author, whose best-known work was turned into a series of world-famous films, was my godfather ?

4 At which course did I ride my first winner in 1963?

5 Which channel did I appear on in my first TV appearance?

6 What happened on my only ride for the Queen Mother?

7 Which famous horse did I ride in a gallop for my first piece as Sunday Times racing correspondent?

8 Who have I not Interviewed on TV - Joan Collins, Ian Botham or Neil Tennant?

9 Why did things not go to plan when I travelled to Trinidad to interview star West Indian cricketer Brian Lara?

10 When I reappeared on ITV Racing in February 2017, 32 years after my last appearance on the channel, the first Twitter comment was "Crikey. Now they've brought Brough Scott out of the . . . " Complete the sentence.

ROUND 27
THE SKY'S THE LIMIT

All the questions relate to the sky above us

1 Which filly won the Oaks by a record 12 lengths? She went on to win the St Leger and finish runner-up in the Arc de Triomphe.

2 Which horse gave jockey Leighton Aspell his second win in the Grand National?

3 Who was once described as the "world's naughtiest horse" for his increasingly aggressive behaviour? He won the 1994 St Leger in a season when he became the first three-year-old to be crowned Europe's Champion Stayer.

4 Which horse finished second in the 1985 Arc de Triomphe but was handed the race in the stewards' room when Sagace was disqualified for causing interference?

5 Which horse in 2009 won a Group 1 race every month from May to October?

6 Which filly gave Richard Hannon Snr his final Classic victory before handing over to his son when landing the 1000 Guineas in 2013?

7 Cloudy Lane ran in three Grand Nationals with his sixth place behind Comply Or Die his best finishing position. Which race did he win over the big Aintree fences?

8 Moon Madness gave which trainer the first of his three St Leger victories?

9 Mighty Thunder was the first winner of the Scottish Grand National for which Scottish trainer?

10 Which horse won his first Group 1 prize at the 16th attempt when landing the 2018 Sussex Stakes?

ROUND 28
THE SUFFRAGETTE DERBY

All the questions relate to the 1913 Derby

1   Which British monarch owned Anmer, the horse brought down by Emily Davison at Tattenham Corner in the 1913 Derby?

2   What was the full name of the 'Suffragette' movement, abbreviated in the initials WSPU?

3   Who founded the WSPU in 1903 and had a prominent role in the movement at the time of the 1913 Derby?

4   The family of Charles Bower Ismay, who owned disqualified 'winner' Craganour, ran which shipping company, which launched RMS Titanic in 1912?

5   What was the starting price of Aboyeur, who was promoted to first place after the stewards found he had been the victim of interference caused by Craganour?

6   What was the nationality of Craganour's jockey, Johnny Reiff?

ROUND 29
WHAT'S IN A NAME

Famous racing figures not always known by their given names

1   Which jockey, who rode the winners of the Champion Hurdle and Gold Cup and was later a successful trainer, had the forenames Herbert Charles Denton?

2   Champion jumps trainer David Nicholson was widely known by a nickname given to him by one of his trainer father's grooms. What was it?

3   Trainer Captain Ryan Price went down in the racecard by his initials HR. What did the 'H' stand for?

4   Which trainer, who twice saddled the winner of the Derby, had the middle name Leeper? His sons, who followed him into the training ranks, also share the same middle name.

5   What surname links the winning, but unrelated, jockeys in the 2016 and 2019 Champion Hurdles?

6   Tony McCoy is often referred to simply by his initials AP. What does the 'P' stand for?

7   Which multiple champion jockey was known by the nickname The Tin Man?

8   Which long-serving national newspaper racing correspondent was known as The Punter's Pal?

9   Which Derby-winning jockey's boyish looks led to him being known as The Choirboy?

10   Which former Royal trainer, who won the Gold Cup at Royal Ascot on three successive occasions, has the middle names Robin Hood having been deemed to be descended from the legendary outlaw?

ROUND 30
FEATHERED FRIENDS

All the questions have some connection to birds

1   Which horse, named after a bird native to Asia and usually found around rivers and estuaries, won the Champion Stakes and Irish Champion Stakes in 1988 having beaten star French filly Miesque in the Prix de Diane the previous year?

2   Which bird has become a much-loved cartoonist in racing circles?

3   Which horse won the County Hurdle at the 2002 Cheltenham Festival before returning the following year to win the Champion Hurdle?

4   My Swallow – champion two-year-old in 1970 and third behind Brigadier Gerard and Mill Reef in the 2000 Guineas – was owned by a TV rentals magnate. The well-known philanthropist, at one time had up to 150 horses in training. Who was he?

5   Who is the only rider to be Irish National Hunt champion jockey on nine consecutive occasions?

6   What is the name of a fence, often found on French racecourses, that is solid at the bottom with several feet of brush sticking out of the top? A fearsome example of this can be found at Auteuil.

7   Which amateur jockey won the Cheltenham Gold Cup on Little Owl in 1981?

8   Which horse gave jockey Mark Dwyer his only Champion Hurdle victory?

9   Before twice winning the Champion Hurdle Sea Pigeon was twice runner-up in the same race to which horse?

10   Which dual winner of the Hardwicke Stakes at Royal Ascot, as well as the Yorkshire Cup and Princess Of Wales's Stakes, was named after a type of penguin?

ROUND 31
IN THE BEGINNING

All the questions relate to the early days of horseracing

1 Oliver Cromwell banned horseracing in 1654. Which King, having been restored to the throne, commissioned the first Newmarket Town Plate race?

2 Which Queen in 1711 founded Ascot racecourse? The opening race of Royal Ascot is named in her honour.

3 Which organisation, formed following a meeting in Pall Mall, was set up regulate horseracing? It took its name from the medieval word for horseman.

4 The oldest race still in existence is thought to be the Kiplingcotes Derby, first run in 1519. In which county is the village of Kiplingcote, where the race is run mostly on fields, farm tracks and verges?

5 The winner of which race is presented with what is reportedly the oldest sporting trophy in the world?

6 Bell's Life of London, which was the racing newspaper of choice in Victorian times, was the forerunner of which newspaper?

7 The naming of the Derby was decided by a coin toss between Lord Derby and which other English aristocrat? He has a handicap named after him at Newmarket's July Meeting.

8 William Wildman and Dennis O'Kelly were, at different times, the owners of which great 18th century horse, who retired unbeaten after 18 races and went on to be a hugely influential stallion? He is commemorated with a Group 1 British Flat race.

9 Which late Victorian American jockey, who revolutionised the style of race-riding in Britain, is remembered by the cockney rhyming slang for being on your own?

10 Which British racecourse, which first staged racing in 1539, is recognised as the oldest venue still to be in operation?

ROUND 32
STARS AND STRIPES

All the questions have a link to America

1   Three races make up the American Triple Crown. The Kentucky Derby, The Belmont Stakes and which other race?

2   Which horse won the Maryland Hunt Cup three times in the 1960s as well as crossing the Atlantic to win the Grand National?

3   Which American jockey rode 8,833 winners from an astonishing 40,350 rides?

4   Which American was the first foreign rider of the modern era to be crowned France's champion jockey?

5   Which American jumps trainer, who retired in January 2021, saddled Flatterer to be runner-up behind See You Then in the 1987 Champion Hurdle?

6   In which American city would you be in if you were at Churchill Downs racecourse?

7   Which horse became the first American-trained winner of a British jumps race when successful in the Chris Coley Racing Hurdle, which is now the Relkeel Hurdle, at Cheltenham in 1992?

8   Which American-trained horse was the first winner of the Dubai World Cup?

9   Which horse, trained by American Mark Casse, won the 2016 Queen Anne Stakes at Royal Ascot?

10   At which racecourse was the inaugural Breeders' Cup held in 1984?

ROUND 33
MASKED TRAINERS

Identify the National Hunt trainers in their Covid masks

Photos courtesy of focusonracing.com

ROUND 34
RANK OUTSIDER

All the questions relate to horses who made an impact at massive odds

1   He Knows No Fear won a race at Leopardstown in August 2020 at which record-breaking odds?

2   As of 2021, what was the last horse to win the Grand National at 100-1?

3   Which jockey won the Derby on 40-1 outsider Wings Of Eagles, trained by Aidan O'Brien, at Epsom in 2017? It was only his fourth winner in more than two years.

4   Nando Parrado, sent off at 150-1, won which race at Royal Ascot in 2020?

5   Intercessor won a Flat novice race at Newbury in 2020 at odds of 200-1 when he was ridden by which son of a former champion jockey?

6   Hot favourite Nashwan won the 1989 Derby but which 500-1 shot finished runner-up?

7   Who rode 100-1 shot Norton's Coin to win the 1990 Cheltenham Gold Cup?

8   Which Irish trainer won the 1991 Oaks at Epsom with 50-1 shot Jet Ski Lady?

9   Which horse won the 1989 Champion Hurdle at 50-1 – the biggest price of any winner of the race?

10   Which trainer, after winning the 2004 Cambridgeshire Handicap at Newmarket with 100-1 shot Spanish Don, joked that "it was my popularity that made him that price"?

ROUND 35
FOOTBALL CRAZY

All the questions have a football connection to racing

1 Which League One club did Ireland international striker Aiden O'Brien, namesake of the Irish trainer, join from Millwall in the summer of 2020?

2 Which international goalkeeper owned a horse called Between The Sticks? She won her first two races, beating subsequent Cheveley Park Stakes winner Dead Certain at Windsor in May 1989, but never won again.

3 Which England international footballer trained more than 150 winners between 1988 and 1996? Among his notable horses were Young Jason, Sir Harry Hardman and Allwight Then.

4 Mick Channon famously switched to training racehorses after a successful football career. What was the name of his first Classic winner, who won the 2012 Irish 1,000 Guineas?

5 Before Channon's training career took off he bred the winner of the Tote Gold Trophy (now the Betfair Hurdle) at Newbury. What was his name?

6 Which horse, owned by Liverpool footballers Robbie Fowler and Steve McManaman, won seven chases as a novice in 2001/02 and was runner-up behind Moscow Flyer in the Arkle Trophy at the Cheltenham Festival?

7 Which horse, owned and bred by England striker Michael Owen, won the King George V Handicap at Royal Ascot in 2011, before adding the Ormonde Stakes, Goodwood Cup and Irish St Leger to his big-race haul?

8 Which England international, who played for Chelsea, Liverpool and Portsmouth among others, owned horses called Use Your Filbert, Drinkuptrig and Rainbow Orse?

9 Rock Of Gibraltar, part-owned by Sir Alex Ferguson, won how many Group 1 races in his career?

10 Dual Ayr Gold Cup winner Funfair Wane raced in the colours of which international footballer and manager's wife?

ROUND 36
GREY DAYS

All the questions are related to famous grey horses

1   Which grey chaser, trained by Susan Nock, landed the notable double of Cheltenham's two big pre-Christmas handicap chases in 1997?

2   After watching him win a Newcastle novices' hurdle in 1992, about which horse did Arthur Stephenson remark "just wait until you see him over the black ones"? Sadly, the veteran trainer died before he ran over fences.

3   Who rode Neptune Collonges to win the Grand National by a nose in 2012?

4   Which racecourse hosts a handicap specifically for grey horses?

5   Which horse ended his career with victory in the Breeders' Cup Turf in 1999. His earlier wins included the Eclipse, Coronation Cup and King George VI and Queen Elizabeth Stakes?

6   Which American horse, known as the 'Gray Ghost', suffered his only defeat in 22 races when runner-up in the 1953 Kentucky Derby? He bounced back to win the Preakness and Belmont Stakes.

7   Roy Rocket, trained by John Berry, won nine races at which racecourse between 2015 and 2018 but never won anywhere else?

8   Which horse was rumoured to be the target of dopers before winning the 1961 Grand National? High Spot, a similar-looking horse, was put in his box as a decoy in the days leading up to the race.

9   Which horse won the Dante Stakes, French Derby and Irish Champion Stakes in 2014 for trainer Kevin Ryan?

10   Which grey gave Pat Eddery his 4,000 winner when he landed the 1997 St Leger?

WHAT'S ON THE MENU?

All the questions or answers have a food theme

1 Which horse won the Irish Gold Cup on three occasions? He was ridden by Timmy Murphy, Paul Carberry and Andrew McNamara.

2 Michael Scudamore, father of Peter and grandfather of Tom and Michael, won the 1959 Grand National on which horse?

3 Who owned and trained Prideaux Boy to win the 1986 Lanzarote Hurdle? His company was one of the country's biggest suppliers of pork, bacon and cooked meats and his colours were later carried to great success by the likes of dual Champion Chaser Viking Flagship.

4 Which horse, who was clearly a bit fruity, finished runner-up at four consecutive Cheltenham Festivals between 2017 and 2020?

5 Which horse, named after a Christmas staple, won 12 all-weather races for trainer Gary Moore?

6 Barrie Cope's food stalls were a familiar sight on racecourses for decades. What type of food was he associated with?

7 Which biscuit gave its name to the winner of the 2018 Weatherbys Super Sprint at Newbury for trainer Richard Hannon and jockey Harry Bentley?

8 Which horse won the 1989 Whitbread Gold Cup and went off favourite for the Grand National the following year? He was named after a consommé made from calves feet popular in Victorian times, which later became slang for a soup containing questionable ingredients?

9 Which horse, named after a variety of curry, gave Australian training legend Bart Cummings the 11th of his record 12 Melbourne Cup victories when successful in 1999?

10 What is the name of the company – purveyors of a revered delicacy – who started sponsoring the December Gold Cup at Cheltenham in 2014?

ROUND 38
RACECOURSE LAYOUTS

Identify the Flat courses from their track layouts - the maps are not necessarily to scale

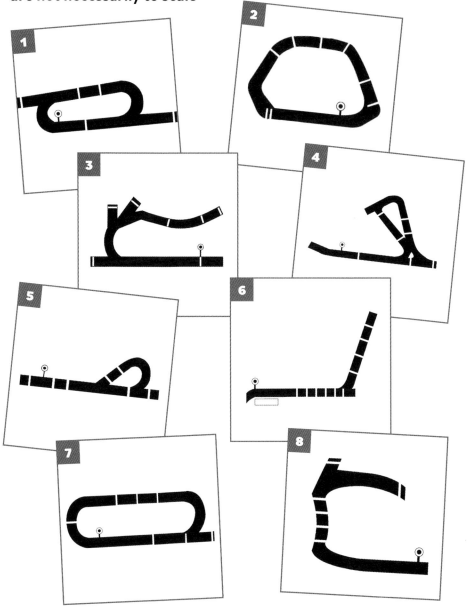

ROUND 39
THOSE WHO PAY THE BILLS

All the questions relate to prominent owners

1   Which owner enjoyed his first British success when Hatta won at Brighton in 1977?

2   Which infamous gangsters owned a horse, which failed to win a race, called Solway Cross?

3   Industrialist David Brown, famous for owning Aston Martin, owned the 1957 Cheltenham Gold Cup winner Linwell. As well as cars, Brown is well known for manufacturing which other vehicles?

4   Which Grand National-winning owner made his fortune manufacturing toys including Teletubbies and Thomas The Tank Engine?

5   Which American businessman and US ambassador to Ireland owned Derby winner Sir Ivor and dual Cheltenham Gold Cup winner L'Escargot?

6   Lester Piggott described which French art dealer and his family as "inveterate bad losers"?

7   The mother of which current Classic-winning trainer owned 1982 Cheltenham Gold Cup winner Silver Buck?

8   Baroness Dido Harding hit the headlines in 2020 when put in charge of the NHS Test And Trace programme as part of the government's response to the Covid-19 pandemic. Which Cheltenham Gold Cup winner did she own?

9   Insurance loss assessor Henry Alper owned which three-time Champion Hurdler?

10   Oaks and St Leger heroine User Friendly and Coral-Eclipse winner Environment Friend ran in the colours of which owner-breeder?

ROUND 40
SCANDAL AND SKULLDUGGERY

All the questions are connected to some of the darker moments in racing

1   A group of Irish gamblers attempted to pull off a betting coup at Cartmel in 1974. Many bookmakers refused to pay out and the ringleaders ended up in court. What was the name of the horse involved?

2   Which multiple champion jockey was given a six-month ban for pulling Stuart Webster from his horse after the finish of a race at Beverley in 1994?

3   Which champion jumps trainer appeared before the Jockey Club accused of hitting photographer Edward Whitaker following the 1994 King George? He was fined £1,500 for using obscene language and threatening behaviour.

4   Godolphin trainer Mahmood Al Zarooni was disqualified from racing for eight years in 2013 after admitting administering steroids to 15 horses at his Newmarket yard. Which horse did he train to win the 2012 St Leger?

5   Which flamboyant gambler and racehorse owner, once estimated to be worth £150million, was jailed in 1997 for breaching the Insolvency Act? His best horses were Katies, Stearsby and Mr Snugfit.

6   Jenny Pitman was fined £200 for improper conduct after hitting which jockey at Ayr's Scottish National meeting in 1990?

7   It was claimed, but never proven, that sonic binoculars were used to force a horse to swerve and unship its jockey at Royal Ascot in 1988. What was the name of the horse?

8   In a heated exchange broadcast live on television, Barney Curley repeatedly called which former jockey-turned TV presenter an "underachiever"?

9   Which Cheltenham Gold Cup-winning jockey was banned for two months in 1982 for betting £50 on a 1-2 favourite with an on-course bookmaker at Cartmel?

10   Ex-policeman Graham Piper named one of his horses after which Scotland Yard detective, famous for tackling the Kray twins? Piper was later jailed for 14 years for his part in drugs smuggling.

ROUND 41
TARTAN ARMY

All the questions relate to Scotland

1 Which Scot trained One For Arthur to win the 2017 Grand National?

2 Which Scottish jockey was the first female rider to become champion conditional jockey?

3 Formerly known as Edinburgh racecourse, by what name is it known today?

4 Prolific National Hunt trainer Len Lungo retired in 2009. Which trainer now based at the same stables at Carrutherstown, near Dumfries, won the 2017 Ebor Handicap?

5 The Glasgow Stakes, which used to be a Derby trial, was transferred to Hamilton Park in 2006 from which racecourse?

6 Which Scottish rugby international was the owner of 1979 Grand National winner Rubstic?

7 Which winner of the Supreme Novices' Hurdle tragically died as a result of injuries sustained in a last-flight fall in the 1978 Scottish Champion Hurdle?

8 Which rider, born in Stirling in 1942, was British Champion Flat Jockey five times?

9 In 1947 which Scottish racecourse was the first in the UK to hold an evening meeting?

10 In which Scottish city was Sir Henry Cecil born?

ROUND 42
STABLE LIFE

Name the trainer from his/her stables

1 Who trains at Heath House?

2 Who trains at Pond House?

3 Who trains at Kingsley House?

4 Who trains at Sandhill Racing Stables?

5 Who trains at Clarehaven Stables?

6 Who trains at Ravenswell Farm?

7 Who trains at Seven Barrows?

8 Who trains at Grange Hill Farm?

9 Who trains at Musley Bank Stables?

10 Who trains at Fitzroy House Stables?

ROUND 43
THE NUMBER BOARD

All the answers are numbers

1 How many fences are jumped by the winner of the Grand National?

2 How many racecourses were actively operating in Britain in 2021?

3 What is the maximum field size in the Grand National?

4 When Frodon won the 2020 King George VI Chase it took Paul Nicholls' tally in the race to how many victories?

5 After how many winners does a conditional jump jockey lose his claim?

6 How many racecourse are there in Scotland?

7 Glorious Goodwood consists of how many days?

8 How many times was Sir Gordon Richards champion jockey?

9 Frankel was unbeaten in 14 races. How many were Group 1 prizes?

10 How many fences are jumped in the Cheltenham Gold Cup?

ROUND 44
GUESS WHO

Identify the famous racing personality

ROUND 45
SCREEN STARS

All the questions relate to racing on television and in films

1 In one of the stories by Sir Arthur Conan Doyle and part of ITV's popular adaption, Sherlock Holmes tracked down a champion racehorse who had gone missing from his Dartmoor stables. What was his name?

2 What was the racing-based BBC drama series, screened in 1991 and 1992, starring Mark Greenstreet, Susannah York and David McCallum, called?

3 In the Only Fools And Horse episode 'A Royal Flush', Del Boy tells the Duke of Maylebury he recognises him from his picture in The Sporting Life. What is the name of the of the Derby hopeful he mentions which gave name to a horse, trained by Richard Spencer, that made its debut in a Wincanton bumper in 2018?

4 Who played the part of trainer Josh Gifford in the film Champions, based on the famous Grand National victory of Aldaniti and Bob Champion?

5 The story of Dream Alliance, the horse bred by a barmaid and raised on a South Wales allotment, sparked the films Dark Horse and Dream Horse. In which race did he enjoy his finest hour?

6 Tobey Maguire played jockey Red Pollard in a film about which champion American racehorse?

7 Racing TV is based in which film studios made famous by comedies and, more recently, Downton Abbey?

8 Which racing broadcaster appeared opposite Benedict Cumberbatch in a Harrow School production of The Taming Of The Shrew?

9 Ride Like A Girl told the story of jockey Michelle Payne's victory in which world famous race?

10 Which actor, singer-songwriter and comedian of the 1930s and '40s is thought to be the youngest ever professional jockey? He rode in races aged 10 in 1915 before going on to become Britain's highest paid entertainer of his era.

ROUND 46
ON THE TROT

All the questions relate to winning sequences

1   Which is the only horse to have won four consecutive Goodwood Cups?

2   Which horse won six consecutive David Nicholson Mares' Hurdles?

3   Which horse won the Stayers' Hurdle at the Cheltenham Festival on four consecutive occasions?

4   Which horse won the Queen Alexandra Stakes at Royal Ascot on six consecutive occasions between WWI and WWII?

5   Which horse finished runner-up in three consecutive Champion Hurdles? He was twice second behind his stablemate Istabraq.

6   Which horse won the Gold Cup at Royal Ascot four times between 2006 and 2009?

7   Which horse won the Cheltenham Gold Cup five times in the 1930s?

8   Which horse, trained by Barry Hills, won the Jockey Club Cup at Newmarket five years on the bounce in the 1990s?

9   Who is the only horse to have won Australia's Cox Plate on four consecutive occasions?

10   Which jockey rode six consecutive winners over two days at Ffos Las in August 2021?

ODDS COMPILERS

All the questions relate to racecourse betting and odds

1   How many bets are in a Yankee?

2   If a horse is described as a 'rag' in betting terms what does it mean?

3   How much is a 'monkey'?

4   What do you call a multiple bet consisting of six selections and 57 bets?

5   What is betting slang for the price 100-30?

6   In 1999 the Tote linked up with Channel 4 Racing to introduce which bet where punters had to pick the winner of six televised races?

7   To which company was the Tote sold in 2011?

8   Bookmakers pay greyhound tracks to hold meetings, specifically to be televised in their shops. What are they called?

9   If a tic-tac man had touched the top of his head with both hands what price would he have been relaying?

10   French businessman Pierre Oller introduced one of the world's most popular methods of betting on horseracing in around 1870. What is it known as today?

HISTORY LESSON

All the questions relate to historical characters or features

1 Which astronomer, often referred to as the 'father of modern science', won the Derby, Irish Derby and the King George VI And Queen Elizabeth Diamond Stakes in 2001?

2 Which triple Champion Hurdle winner was named after a series of battles at Thermopylae and Marathon?

3 Which horse, dubbed the 'spotted wonder', was recognised as the best two-year-old of the 20th century and was the title given to the infamous king who ordered the execution of Jesus and John the Baptist?

4 Which historic Roman road linking Dover, London and Wroxeter, won a wartime Derby for owner Lord Derby?

5 Which horse, who won both the 2000 Guineas and the Derby in 2012, was also a castle and court associated with King Arthur?

6 Which horse, who won the 2000 Guineas in 2006 but sadly fractured his canon bone in the Breeders' Cup Classic the following year, was also the first president of the United States?

7 Which horse, who won the 2000 Guineas, Irish 2,000 Guineas, St James's Palace Stakes and Sussex Stakes in 2008, was also the commonly used name for one of the central figures in the Portuguese Empire, Henrique of Portugal?

8 Which horse gave Lester Piggott his final Classic win and was also a Spanish sailor who was the first to spot land on Christopher Columbus' ship La Pinta as it sailed through the Caribbean Sea?

9 Which horse, named after a High King of Ireland from the 11th Century, gave Jamie Spencer his first, and as of 2021, St Leger victory?

10 Which horse, named after a philosopher of Ancient Greece, gave George Duffield and Aidan O'Brien a Group 1 victory in what is now known as the Vertem Futurity Trophy at Doncaster in 1999?

SHERGAR KIDNAPPED

All the questions relate to the kidnapping of 1981 Derby winner Shergar

THE STANDARD CITY PRICES
Wednesday, February 9, 1983   17p   *Incorporating the* Evening News

Shergar £2m ransom demand

DERBY WINNER STOLEN

1 Which race did Shergar win by 12 lengths immediately before heading to Epsom for the Derby?

2 Walter Swinburn rode Shergar to his record ten-length Derby victory but he was suspended when he won the Irish Derby. Who took over in the saddle?

3 What was the name of the Aga Khan's stud in Co Kildare, Ireland, where Shergar was kidnapped from?

4 Why was 'King Neptune' significant in the kidnapping of Shergar?

5 The kidnappers insisted negotiations would only take place with three prominent racing journalists. John Oaksey, Peter Campling and which other broadcaster?

6 The Shergar Cup, a jockeys' team competition, was created in 1999 and is still held today. At which racecourse did the first Shergar Cup take place?

ROUND 50
IT'S A COLOURFUL LIFE

Identify which owners' horses carried these famous racing colours

1   Which British politician's racing colours were: chocolate, pink sleeves and cap?

2   Which former owner/trainer/gambler's racing colours were: black, white hooped sleeves, red and white hooped cap?

3   Which owner, who won the Cheltenham Gold Cup, Champion Hurdle, Grand National and the Derby, had the racing colours: blue, yellow hoop, blue sleeves with yellow armlet, yellow cap with blue hoop?

4   Which football manager's racing colours are: red, white stars on sleeves, white cap with red star?

5   Which famous rock star's racing colours are: white, red sash, red sleeves and cap?

6   Which two footballers owned horses together that had the racing colours: white, blue star on cap?

7   Which successful racing syndicate has the colours: green and red diablo, white sleeves with green diamonds, white cap with red diamond?

8   Which comedian, musical hall performer of World War II and member of the Crazy Gang entertainers, first registered the famous racing colours: harlequin, otherwise known as crazy quilt?

9   Which former football manager and current TV personality's racing colours are: dark blue with blue seams, white sleeves, red and white striped cap?

10   Which member of a 1970s chart-topping pop group, now a successful racehorse breeder, has the racing colours: black and grey check, black sleeves and cap?

ROUND 51
PETER SCUDAMORE

1 Which famous star did I ride against in a charity race at Lingfield? Once an apprentice jockey, he went on to make his name as an actor and musician with an American pop band, who had their own TV show.

2 On which horse did I twice win the Welsh Grand National?

3 Who trained Remainder Man to be placed in both the 2000 Guineas and the Derby in 1978? All three Scudamore jockeys, dad Michael, son Tom and I all rode winners for him?

4 Sir Charles won the 1950 Supreme Novices' Hurdle but why was his victory important to the Scudamore family?

5 Between us, Tom and I have ridden the winner of which famous race on five occasions? Our winners were: Strands Of Gold, Chatham (Peter) Madison du Berlais, Sizing Tennessee, Cloth Cap (Tom).

6 I never rode the winner of the King George but dad and Tom did. Name the horses.

7 In 2000, Tom finished fifth in an amateur riders' race at Towcester. The race was won by Mersey Beat ridden by which subsequent champion jockey?

8 My son Michael trained Monbeg Dude to win the 2012 Welsh National. Which jockey rode him to victory with what is considered one of the great steeplechase rides?

9 My second cousin Richard Scudamore was firstly chief executive and then executive chairman of which high-profile sporting organisation?

10 Tom won the race where his grandfather's trophy for winning the Grand National is presented to the winner. Where is it run?

ROUND 52
RYAN MOORE

1 For which professional football club did I have trials?

2 When I was Champion Apprentice in 2003 I was attached to which trainer?

3 Which horse gave me my first Group 1 winner when landing the Juddmonte International at York in 2006?

4 On which horse did I win the Derby and Arc de Triomphe in the same season?

5 In whose colours did I win the Gold Cup at Royal Ascot in 2013 on Estimate?

6 In 2014 I rode Protectionist, trained by Andreas Wohler in Germany, to win which famous race?

7 Which Classic did I win in successive years on Capri and Kew Gardens?

8 Which horse, trained by Sir Michael Stoute, did I ride to win the Breeders' Cup Turf in both 2008 and 2009?

9 Snow Fairy gave me Group 1 wins all around the world including the Oaks, Irish Oaks, the Hong Kong Cup and Japan's Queen Elizabeth II Cup twice. Who trained her?

10 Which horse, trained my dad Gary and ridden by my brother Jamie, won the Champion Chase at the 2014 Cheltenham Festival?

ROUND 53
LUKE HARVEY

1 Which trainer, who I was working for at his stables in Letcombe Bassett near Lambourn, gave me my first ride?

2 My only Cheltenham Festival winner came on Taberna Lord in 1987. Who was the trainer?

3 The closest I came to riding another Festival winner was in what is now the Ultima Chase in 1993 when the horse I was riding, Country Member, was beaten a short head by Givus A Buck. Who was the winning jockey?

4 Why is the horse Porlock Bay special to me?

5 What was the name of the jockey I rode against who started as a broadcaster on the original Racing Channel at the same time as me?

6 What was the name of the Channel 4 documentary that featured Carl Llewellyn, Richard Guest and myself?

7 Which horse did I ride to win the SGB Chase in 1989? The race is now run as the Ascot Silver Cup.

8 Cool Ground had a number of trainers during his career. Who was his trainer when I won the Welsh Grand National on him?

9 With which former Flat jockey did I co-present 'Get In' on the Attheraces TV channel?

10 I'm now based near Cheltenham Racecourse at the foot of the hill that provides such a stunning back drop to the home of jump racing. What is the name of that hill?

ROUND 54
DAVID YATES

1   I am a proud son of Bedford, but which British racecourse is nearest, as the crow flies, to my birthplace in the town's North Wing hospital?

2   My first Derby-winning selection in the Daily Mirror was the Sir Michael Stoute-trained Kris Kin in 2003, but who rode the colt to victory in his Epsom trial, the Dee Stakes at Chester?

3   The Victorian great Fred Archer is a hero of mine. How many consecutive jockeys' titles did he win before ending his own life weeks before his 30th birthday?

4   My first front-page splash for the Daily Mirror was an interview with Kieren Fallon after his arrest as part of a doomed City of London Police investigation into race fixing. In which year was the dawn raid?

5   I celebrated Aliysa's win in the 1989 Oaks by an all-night boozing session in London, followed by an illegal entry into France by scaling an 8ft fence at Calais. For traces of which banned substance was the Aga Khan's filly later disqualified?

6   During my 2014 Land's End to John O'Groats bike ride in aid of Racing Welfare – I don't normally like to talk about my charity work – I stopped off for a 'bucket shake' at which racecourse, where the Mark Johnston-trained Alex My Boy won the feature race, the Archerfield Cup?

7   In the capital of England, I am regularly saluted by local people as 'The Top Hat Man Of Old London Town' thanks to my sideline Silk Toppers, which offers for sale antique silk top hats at very reasonable prices. How many days' racing in Britain are top hats traditionally worn?

8   The single most taking performance over jumps I've seen was Denman's destruction of his rivals in the 2008 Cheltenham Gold Cup. Which former jockey, who won the race during his career in the saddle, sold the horse to Paul Nicholls?

9   Epsom is my favourite racecourse and the Cazoo Derby my best-loved race. Which is the last horse to win the great race on his seasonal reappearance?

10   Away from the races, I like nothing better than a night at the opera. Who rode the Sir Michael Stoute-trained – and Sheikh Mohammed-owned – Opera House to lift the 1993 Coral-Eclipse Stakes?

ROUND 55
SET YOUR SATNAV

Guess the name of the racecourse from its postcode

1   Which racecourse has the postcode WA12 0HQ?

2   Which racecourse has the postcode NP16 6BE?

3   Which racecourse has the postcode ST14 8BD?

4   Which racecourse has the postcode KA8 0JE?

5   Which racecourse has the postcode LS22 5EJ?

6   Which racecourse has the postcode NR21 7NY?

7   Which racecourse has the postcode BA9 8BJ?

8   Which racecourse has the postcode LL13 0DA?

9   Which racecourse has the postcode SY8 2BT?

10   Which racecourse has the postcode YO7 1QL?

ROUND 56
RACING GOLFERS

Identify the racing personalities all of whom were taking part in one of Jim Old's IJF Golf Days

Photos courtesy of Gavin James and Bryan Mathieson

ROUND 57
THE GREATEST

All the questions relate to the greatest horses, greatest races, greatest jockeys, greatest trainers and greatest characters

1 Which champion jockey-turned broadcaster did Channel 4 colleague John McCririck often refer to as the greatest jockey?

2 At which course did Lester Piggott makes his riding comeback in 1990?

3 AP McCoy won his only Grand National on which horse?

4 Who trained Foinavon to win the 1967 Grand National at 100-1 when most of the field was wiped out at the fence that now bears the horse's name?

5 Annie Power, winner of the 2016 Champion Hurdle, had previously finished runner-up in which Cheltenham Festival race?

6 Who is the most successful trainer in the history of the Champion Hurdle?

7 Lester Piggott's daughter Maureen is married to which current trainer?

8 Pat Eddery won the Arc de Triomphe in three consecutive years in the 1980s. Which horse completed that hat-trick?

9 Which horse, who went on to win the King George VI and Queen Elizabeth Stakes and the Coral-Eclipse Stakes, finished runner-up behind Frankel on his debut?

10 Which jockey rode Stradivarius to win the Goodwood Cup in 2017 and 2018?

ROUND 58
TROPHY HUNTERS

Identify which course you would be at if you were watching these famous races

1 At which course would you be if you were watching the Kingwell Hurdle?

2 At which course would you be if you were watching the Nunthorpe Stakes?

3 At which course would you be if you were watching Haldon Gold Cup?

4 At which course would you be if you were watching the Cathedral Stakes?

5 At which course would you be if you were watching the Nassau Stakes?

6 At which racecourse would you be if you were watching the Welsh Champion Hurdle?

7 At which course would you be if you were watching the Ormonde Stakes?

8 At which course would you be if you were watching the Peterborough Chase?

9 At which course would you be if you were watching the Winter Derby?

10 At which course would you be if you were watching the Eclipse Stakes?

ROUND 59
AUSSIE RULES

All the questions relate to Australia

1   The Everest is the richest race run in Australia and it was the world's most valuable turf race when it was launched in 2017. Where is it run?

2   Which Australian jockey rode more than 100 winners in Britain for 10 successive seasons between 1955 and 1964?

3   Which horse won the French 2000 Guineas for Aidan O'Brien and Kieren Fallon in 2006?

4   Which legendary Australian trainer was responsible for 12 Melbourne Cup winners?

5   Which Australian sprinter retired undefeated in 2013 having won 25 races including the Diamond Jubilee Stakes at Royal Ascot?

6   In which Australian city does 'the race that stops a nation' take place?

7   True or False. Australia has more racecourses than any other country in the world?

8   In which Australian city might you visit Ascot racecourse?

9   Which Australian took over from Sir Peter O'Sullevan as BBC senior commentator in 1997?

10 In 2018 Cross Counter became the first British-trained horse to win which famous Australian race?

ROUND 60
AT THE BAR

All the questions are related to famous racing pubs

1 Which Epsom pub, named after a Derby winner, is famous for having a tip for the Epsom Classic appear in chalk on a wishing well before the big race?

2 The Plough Inn lies at the bottom of which Cheltenham Gold Cup and Grand National-winning trainer's gallops?

3 Which pub is Paul Nicholls' local watering hole?

4 What is the name of the pub that used to be co-owned by Nigel Twiston-Davies and was the venue for many celebrations following big-race wins?

5 Which ex-jockey used to own the Blowing Stone Inn in Kingston Lisle near Lambourn?

6 Anyone walking from which racecourse into the city centre would pass pubs called The Mount, The Bay Horse, The Windmill and The Punchbowl?

7 The Bull, The White Hart and The Waggon and Horses are pubs found on the High Street of which town?

8 The Jubilee pub is situated across the road from which racecourse, which hosts a race of the same name?

9 Which brewery is responsible for the longest commercial sponsorship in British Flat horseracing having backed the same York race since 1960? It was formerly called the Magnet Cup but now just takes the sponsor's name?

10 Which legendary jockey grew up in the King's Arms pub, situated just a few furlongs from Cheltenham Racecourse in Prestbury?

RACECOURSE LAYOUTS

Identify the National Hunt courses from their track layout - the maps are not necessarily to scale

ROUND 62
JOCKEYS' BOARD

Name the jockey from their exploits in other fields

1   Which amateur jockey and later TV presenter founded the Injured Jockeys Fund?

2   Which jockey was beaten on Arkle both times he rode him as an amateur jockey before becoming Chief Executive of the Bank of Ireland?

3   Which amateur jockey worked for David Elsworth and rode more than 30 winners before becoming President of the National Farmers' Union in 2018?

4   Which champion jumps jockey was the 'partner' of two Grand National-winning trainers?

5   Which Derby-winning jockey went on to become Chairman of Swindon Town FC?

6   Which amateur jockey lost a leg while serving in the army in Afghanistan and then rode Rathlin Rose to win the 2017 Royal Artillery Gold Cup?

7   Who played full back for Cambridge University and won the National Hunt Chase at the 1963 Cheltenham Festival as an amateur jockey but is better known as a Derby-winning trainer?

8   Which champion amateur jockey, later three-times champion jumps trainer, developed and manufactures the Tapeta all-weather racing surface?

9   Which Cheltenham Gold Cup-winning jockey is the founder and CEO of Portman Dental Care?

10   Which champion jockey walked to the South Pole and partnered Lilia Kopylova in Strictly Come Dancing after retiring from the saddle?

ROUND 63
BETTER BREEDING

All the questions relate to studs and breeding operations

1 Arkle was born at Ballymacoll Stud, County Meath, Ireland in 1957. At that time the stud belonged to which prominent racehorse owner?

2 On the death of Sheikh Hamden Al Maktoum in March 2021, his horses and his familiar blue-and-white racing colours were officially registered to his breeding operation. What is it called?

3 Which powerful racing and breeding operation has its headquarters at Tweenhills Stud at Hartpury in Gloucestershire?

4 Which stud has registered racing colours of red, white sash with blue cap?

5 How many runners did Michael O'Leary's Gigginstown Stud have in the 2017 Irish Grand National?

6 Which of those horses, a previous winner of the Fairyhouse marathon, was first home of those Gigginstown Stud runners? He finished fourth behind Our Duke.

7 Which World War II fighter pilot, who was awarded the Distinguished Flying Cross for his role in the Battle of Britain, later created Coolmore Stud?

8 Darley is the bloodstock arm of which powerful racing operation?

9 Banstead Manor Stud in Cheveley, Newmarket, is the British headquarters of which global breeding operation?

10 The National Stud is located next to which racecourse?

ROUND 64
STEWARDS ENQUIRY

All the questions relate to disqualifications

1 Which horse was disqualified after testing positive for a banned substance having won the 1980 Cheltenham Gold Cup?

2 Which filly, trained by Henry Cecil, was disqualified following a stewards enquiry having narrowly finished first past the post in the 1000 Guineas in 2010?

3 No Bombs was disqualified after winning a race at Ascot in 1979 after failing a drugs test. What was said to be the source of the positive test?

4 Which Irish chaser was controversially disqualified from the 1988 Whitbread Gold Cup, handing Docklands Express victory?

5 Which horse was disqualified after failing a post-race drugs test due to contaminated feed having finished first in the 2002 Hennessy Gold Cup (now the Ladbrokes Trophy)? The result was confirmed nearly two years after the race following a lengthy appeal.

6 Which subsequent Champion Hurdler winner was controversially disqualified after finishing first by five lengths in the Gold Cup at Royal Ascot in 1988?

7 The disqualification of Aliysa as winner of the 1989 Oaks after testing positive for a banned substance prompted which powerful owner to withdraw from British racing?

8 Rock Roi was disqualified after finishing first past the post in successive years (1971 and 1972) of which Group 1 race?

9 Why was 50-1 shot Mandarin Princess disqualified after winning a race for two-year-olds at Yarmouth in 2017? Bizarrely, the result stood for betting purposes.

10 Which horse was disqualified after winning the 2015 St Leger, handing Bondi Beach the race, but was later reinstated after a successful appeal?

ROUND 65
TIPPING LINE

All the questions relate to racing tipsters

1 Lionel Cureton was the first national newspaper tipster to use which famous nom de plume?

2 Which charismatic tipster, a regular sight on racecourses from the 1920s up to his death in 1965, used to attract punters by shouting "I gotta horse"?

3 Which newspaper publishes the racing tips of Robin Goodfellow?

4 One of the Daily Mirror's tipsters is named after the street, just off Fleet Street, where the paper was once based?

5 Racing Post tipster Tom Segal is known for writing which long-running column?

6 Which journalist wrote of his pre-Christmas attempt to win £1,000 for charity in his 'Grab A Grand' column in the Racing Post?

7 Which American journalist, the racing correspondent of The Washington Post from 1978 until his retirement in 2016, was one of the pioneers of collating speed figures? He wrote four books on the subject and the figures still bear his name.

8 Which newspaper discontinued the tipping nom de plume Hotspur when Jim A McGrath left the company in 2014?

9 The non de plume Augur was the chief tipster of which newspaper?

10 Which tipping nom de plume has been used by journalists Bob Butchers, Charlie Fawcus and David Yates?

ROUND 66
MASKED TRAINERS

Identify the flat trainers in their Covid masks

ROUND 67
LUCK OF THE IRISH

All the questions relate to Ireland

1   Which Irishman is the only jockey to ride the winners of the Grand National, Cheltenham Gold Cup and a Group 1 Flat race?

2   Which Gold Cup-winning Irish chaser was named after a mountain in northern Scotland?

3   Which Irish-trained chaser won the inaugural Mackeson Gold Cup in 1960 and returned to Cheltenham to win the same race two years later? He also won the Champion Chase and the Irish Grand National as well as finishing runner-up in two Cheltenham Gold Cups.

4   Which horse gave Aidan O'Brien his first victory in the Irish Derby?

5   Which Irish hurdler won a record 22 Grade 1 races during his career?

6   Which Irish racecourse is situated in Foxrock?

7   Which Irish stayer became the first horse trained in the northern hemisphere to win the Melbourne Cup when successful in 1993?

8   Which horse won the Irish St Leger four times between 2001 and 2004?

9   Which Irish trainer won 16 British Classics and 27 Irish Classics as well as four Cheltenham Gold Cups and three consecutive Grand Nationals?

10   Which Irish jockey rode the first of his 59 Cheltenham Festival winners when Alexander Banquet won the Champion Bumper in 1998?

ROUND 68
LIFE BENEATH THE WAVES

All the questions relate to sealife

1   Which horse won both the Derby and the Arc de Triomphe in 1965? He had a Timeform rating of 145, which is second only to Frankel.

2   Which horse finished third in the 2012 Grand National when his jockey became the first female rider to finished placed in the race?

3   Which horse won the New Derby – a wartime substitute for the Derby and run at Newmarket – in 1944?

4   Champion Hurdler Salmon Spray has a race named in his honour at which course?

5   Which American horse's statute stands proudly both at Santa Anita racecourse and the National Museum of Horseracing in Saratoga Springs?

6   Who rode The Last Samurai to finish runner-up in the 2016 Grand National?

7   Which horse won the 1947 Derby after Gordon Richards turned down the ride in favour of hot favourite Tudor Minstrel?

8   When Crystal Ocean was beaten a head by Enable in the 2019 King George VI and Queen Elizabeth Diamond Stakes he was officially rated the best horse in Britain at that time, a pound ahead of the dual Arc winning filly. What was his rating?

9   Francois Doumen's dual Stayers' Hurdle winner Baracouda beat which horse into second when landing the 2000 Long Walk Hurdle at Ascot on his first run in Britain?

10   Which horse gave Aidan O'Brien his first Ebor win when he landed the historic York handicap in 2001?

ROUND 69
THE SMITHS

All the questions relate to Smiths

1 When Channel 4 took over televising the Grand National from the BBC in 2013 who was sponsoring the race for the first time?

2 Which jockey in 1965 rode Jay Trump to win the Grand National and finish third in the Grand Steeple-Chase de Paris?

3 A blacksmith who solely shoes horses is known as what?

4 Who trained Red Alligator to win the Grand National and was also the first trainer to train 50 winners in consecutive National Hunt and Flat seasons?

5 Who hung up his riding boots in 1994 after 21 years in the saddle and 861 winners including a hat-trick of Champion Hurdles?

6 What is the name of the field that is home to Guards Polo Club on Windsor Great Park near Ascot Racecourse?

7 Who owned Cheltenham Festival greats Kauto Star and Master Minded?

8 Which leading Flat owner, whose colours were carried to victory in the Derby by Wings Of Eagles, also co-owns the Sandy Lane Hotel in Barbados along with his racing partners?

9 Which trainer won the first Becher Chase in 1992 with Kildimo? She won the same Aintree race ten years later with Ardent Scout?

10 What role did Phil Smith fill regarding the Grand National for 20 years until retiring in 2018? He was succeeded by Martin Greenwood.

ROUND 70
FOR THE LOVE OF IT

All the questions relate to amateur jockeys

1 Which Irish jockey, the most successful amateur rider of all time, made headlines in 2017 when he innocently wandered past the ITV cameras in the Cheltenham weighing room completely naked?

2 Which Old Etonian, now the Daily Telegraph's racing correspondent, rode Mr Frisk to win the Grand National?

3 Which amateur jockey, the grandson of a former Lord Mayor of London, won six races around the Grand National course making him the most successful jockey of the modern era over Aintree's unique fences?

4 Which amateur jockey twice passed the post first in the Whitbread Gold Cup, although he lost one in the stewards' room when the race was handed to The Dikler after an objection?

5 The answer to question 4 also bred and part-owned the winner of the 2011 Hennessy Gold Cup with a horse that took its name from his favourite joke. What was the horse called?

6 Which amateur jockey rode a double at the 1987 Cheltenham Festival, including a win on the appropriately named Gee A?

7 Which successful jumps trainer, as an amateur jockey, rode Marcolo in the 1988 Grand National? The pair fell at Becher's Brook.

8 Who became the first female jockey to win a race at the Cheltenham Festival when she rode Eliogarty to victory in the 1983 Foxhunters' Chase?

9 Which amateur jockey ended his riding career by finishing ninth on Upton Grey - a horse owned by Queen Elizabeth The Queen Mother - at Newton Abbot in May 1981?

10 Which Gold Cup winning jockey rode his mother-in-law's Willie Wumpkins to win the Coral Golden Hurdle final - now the Pertemps Final - in three successive years?

ROUND 71
RACING AROUND THE WORLD

Guess which country you would be in if you were at these international racecourses

1   In which country would you be if you were watching racing at Moonee Valley?

2   In which country would you be if you were watching racing at Garrison Savannah?

3   In which country would you be if you were watching racing at Phar Lap Raceway?

4   In which country would you be if you were watching racing at Flamingo Park?

5   In which country would you be if you were watching racing at Oi?

6   In which country would you be if you were watching racing at Kincsem?

7   In which country would you be if you were watching racing at Happy Valley?

8   In which country would you be if you were watching racing at Hipodrom Most?

9   In which country would you be if you were watching racing at Ngong?

10   In which country would you be if you were watching racing at Ooty?

ROUND 72
DEVON LOCH GRAND NATIONAL MYSTERY

All the questions relate to the 1956 Grand National

1   No-one has ever been able to explain why Devon Loch skidded to a halt with the Grand National at his mercy but which horse went on to win the race?

2   The winning jockey admitted after the race that he had given up all hope of catching Devon Loch before the bizarre incident 50 yards from the winning post. Who was the fortunate rider of the winner?

3   The owner of Devon Loch famously remarked "oh, that's racing" after watching her horse cruelly have victory snatched away. Who was she?

4   Devon Loch's trainer Peter Cazalet was champion jumps trainer three times and he also excelled at others sports. For which county did he play 22 first-class cricket matches?

5   Devon Loch's jockey Dick Francis went on to become a famous thriller writer. He wrote more than 40 books with a racing theme but which was his first novel?

6   For which newspaper was Dick Francis the racing correspondent for 16 years?

ROUND 73
JONJO O'NEILL

1 I was christened John O'Neill but what is my second name which gives me the name by which most people know me?

2 Which horse did I ride to win both the Cheltenham Gold Cup and the Champion Hurdle?

3 Shortly after coming over from Ireland to work for Gordon Richards, I was allowed to lead up Titus Oates when he ran in the 1972 Cheltenham Gold Cup. Which Irish mare won the race?

4 I've not only ridden a winner over five furlongs at Royal Ascot but I've also ridden the winner of the longest race. What is the race called?

5 I am the only person to have done what as both a jockey and as a trainer?

6 Which horse did I ride to win the Ebor at York in 1979 when he carried 10st? It's still the biggest weight carried to victory in the race.

7 In April 1978 I rode five winners on one day at which course?

8 I rode Sea Pigeon to his first Champion Hurdle win but missed the ride due to injury when he retained his title the following year. Who replaced me as his jockey?

9 In which country did I have to a sign a form consenting to the removal of my leg prior to an operation if the damage to the leg was irreparable?

10 What is the name of the Cotswold training establishment where I've been based since 2001? It is named after the former quarry in which it was built.

RICHARD HOILES

1 My favourite horse ever was the first to win both the big 2m4f Cheltenham handicaps in November and December then the Mackeson and AF Budge in the same season. One of his racing plates hangs over my front door. Which horse did it belong to?

2 Prior to my getting a job in racing I was an accountant working in London. My commute involved a journey on the tube. Which trainer shares his name with one of the stations on the London Underground?

3 During my frequent visits to racecourses in my youth I saw John Francome break Stan Mellor's record for the number of National Hunt winners on Don't Touch. Which track was I at?

4 One of my first big races I commentated on was the 1992 Coral Welsh National where trainer Martin Pipe saddled the first four home. Can you name the four horses?

5 The only Breeders' Cup I attended was at Woodbine where I saw a horse win whom I would call to victory in the Japan Cup in Toyko just over a year later. Can you name the horse and the jockeys who rode him to those two victories?

6 My biggest race commentary during my time in Hong Kong was their Derby won by a horse who had finished 4th in the Irish Derby for Aidan O'Brien. Can you name the horse named after a famous Dutch footballer?

7 During my time covering the Dubai World Cup I once conducted an interview with a 19-year-old whilst he was perched aboard a camel. Who was the rider and which horse, in the Sheikh Hamdan silks, did he partner to victory in the big race?

8 The biggest single influence on my career was South African jockey Felix Coetzee with whom I worked for many years on race tactics and rides. During that time Felix rode a Hong Kong trained sprinter to win 17 consecutive races. What was the name of the horse?

9 One of my other great sporting loves is Crewe Alexandra who I saw twice at Wembley in consecutive seasons winning the Division 2 Play Off Final and then the Johnstone Paint Trophy. Their three goal scorers over those two games all share surnames with current jockeys. What are they?

10 My cricketing county is Somerset whom I have followed since childhood. Which Somerset and England cricketer is now heavily involved in the Bloodstock industry standing Canford Cliffs at the family's Ridgemont Highlands Stud?

DAVID PIPE

1   Miinnehoma won the 1994 Grand National trained by dad. Which comedian owned him?

2   What was my grandfather David's profession?

3   Which father and son have been stable jockey for dad and me?

4   I trained Gaspara to scoop the big bonus for winning the 2007 Imperial Cup and the Fred Winter Handicap Hurdle at the Cheltenham Festival. Who owned him?

5   Dad's first winner was Hit Parade in a Taunton seller in 1975. Which Scottish jockey rode him?

6   Which hurdler, trained by dad, won 11 races during the 1990/91 season, including six races at Cheltenham?

7   Dad had a lot of success in some of the top Flat handicaps. When he won the Cesarewitch with Miss Fara in 2002, which jockey, then a 5lb apprentice, rode her?

8   Which horse won the Ascot Stakes in 2010 and went on to win the Fulke Walwyn Kim Muir Chase at the Cheltenham Festival the following year?

9   For which multiple champion trainer did I ride a point-to-point winner?

10   Which jockey, thought by many to be one of the best riders never to be champion, rode his first winner at the Cheltenham Festival as an amateur for Martin Pipe?

ROUND 76
ED CHAMBERLIN

1 Enable caused a storm in the 2017 Oaks. But why was there an almighty panic in the ITV truck involving Aidan O'Brien's runners earlier that day?

2 Which member of the ITV Racing team has ridden over the Grand National fences and competed at Badminton?

3 Mick Channon, a legend for my team Southampton FC, bred the horse Sir Gordon. Who was it named after?

4 What did Joanne Coleman, the owner of the 2019 Supreme Novices' Hurdle winner Klassical Dream, reveal live on ITV, was in her handbag?

5 Which member of the ITV Racing team did Her Majesty The Queen describe as "a lunatic" after Big Orange won the Gold Cup at Royal Ascot in 2017?

6 What number saddle cloth did one of my favourite horses, Tiger Roll, wear when winning his first Grand National?

7 When calling a thrilling finish at York's Ebor Meeting in 2017, Richard Hoiles produced an epic commentary with the words "Frankie punches the air - he's sure, I'm not". Who was, in fact, the winning jockey?

8 My ITV colleague Andrew Thornton twice won the Great Yorkshire Chase when it was held away from its usual venue of Doncaster. Name the track.

9 The race that got me hooked on the sport was the 1981 Grand National. Aldaniti beat Spartan Missile in of the greatest sporting stories. Who finished third?

10 Music agent and racehorse owner Emma Banks was a regular on ITV Racing during the summer of 2021 due to the exploits of her horses. Which horse carried her colours to victory in the Group 1 Nassau Stakes at Goodwood?

ROUND 77
THIS IS YOUR LIFE

Name the racing figure from their published autobiography

1   Which champion jockey's autobiography was 'Out Of The Shadows'?

2   Which Grand National-winning jockeys' autobiography was 'Riding the Storm'?

3   Which jump jockey, who rode the winners of the Grand National, Cheltenham Gold Cup, Champion Hurdle and Champion Chase, wrote the autobiography 'True Colours'?

4   Which Grand National and Gold Cup-winning trainer wrote the autobiography 'The Glorious Uncertainty'?

5   Which amateur jockey, breeder, journalist and TV pundit wrote the autobiography 'Mince Pie For Starters'?

6   Which champion jockey wrote the autobiography 'Obsessed'?

7   Which racing broadcaster's autobiography was titled 'Calling The Horses'?

8   Which jumps trainer's autobiography was called 'My Colourful Life - From Red To Amber'?

9   Which Cheltenham Gold Cup-winning jockey's autobiography was called 'The Wayward Lad'?

10   Which trainer's autobiography was titled 'Giving A Little Back'?

ROUND 78
VIVE LA FRANCE

All the questions relate to France

1   What is the only track outside Paris to hold Group 1 Flat races in France?

2   Longchamp and Auteuil racecourses are situated less than a mile apart on the fringes of which well-known Paris public park?

3   Who has trained the winner of the Arc de Triomphe a record eight times?

4   Which horse, trained by Nicky Richards, finished runner-up in the Fighting Fifth Hurdle three times before finally winning the Newcastle prize in 2003? He has a race named after him at the same track run on the same day as the Fighting Fifth.

5   Which French-trained horse won the 1994 Cheltenham Gold Cup having previously won the Grand Steeple-Chase de Paris, one of only two horses to complete the double?

6   Which English-trained horse was the only other horse to complete the Cheltenham Gold Cup and Grand Steeple-Chase de Paris double?

7   While Longchamp was being redeveloped in 2016 and 2017, which course hosted the Arc de Triomphe?

8   Which horse, trained by Ferdy Murphy, won what is now the Ballymore Novices' Hurdle at the Cheltenham Festival in 1998 by 14 lengths? He was tragically killed in a training accident before he could realise his potential over fences.

9   Which French-trained horse beat Best Mate to win the Peterborough Chase at Huntingdon and also collected the Finale Juvenile Hurdle, the Feltham Novices' Chase and the Cotswold Chase in his regular visits to Britain?

10   Which horse, trained by Francois Doumen, interrupted Desert Orchid's string of wins in the King George at Kempton when beating the great grey into second in 1987?

FAMILY CONNECTIONS

On the left-hand page there are photos of a father who has a son or daughter on the right-hand page. Match up the father with their offspring

Photos courtesy of focusonracing.com and Bernard Parkin

ROUND 80
THE OLD ENEMY

All the questions relate to famous bookmakers

1   Which bookmaker, widely regarded as the first to recognise the importance of online gambling, moved his head office to Gibraltar in 1999, where he was the largest private employer?

2   Which on-course bookie, who was famous for laying some of the biggest bets at Cheltenham, was robbed by an armed gang on his way back to his hotel during the 2006 Festival?

3   Who launched bet365 in 2001 prior to selling the family's betting shop chain to Coral for £40million? She is widely regarded as the highest paid CEO of any UK company.

4   Which well-known on-course bookie was a regular on Channel 4 Racing's Morning Line programme? His lay of the day feature was named after a German battleship.

5   Which big betting company erected a Hollywood-style sign on Cleeve Hill overlooking Cheltenham racecourse on Gold Cup day in 2010? The sign was, in fact, bigger than the Hollywood version.

6   Which Scottish bookmaker drove a yellow Rolls Royce and gave out yellow badges for punters to wear at the races? He was warned off for three years in 1978 for paying for information.

7   Who was born Joseph Kagarlitski in 1904 and began his bookmaking business in 1926?

8   Which bookmaker was instrumental in safeguarding the future of the Grand National in the 1970s when Aintree was sold to property developers?

9   Which national newspaper launched a short-lived online betting company in 2016?

10 What is on-course bookie Mickey Fletcher's nickname? He picked up the moniker as a child when he used to sell a particular vegetable to track bookies.

ROUND 81
GLOBETROTTERS

Identify the nationality of these famous international jockeys

1   What nationality is former British champion Flat jockey Michael Roberts?

2   What nationality is American Triple Crown-winning jockey Victor Espinoza?

3   What nationality is British Group 1-winning jockey Yutaka Take?

4   What nationality is St Leger-winning jockey Kerrin McEvoy, who had a spell as Godolphin's second jockey in Britain behind Frankie Dettori?

5   What nationality is Kentucky Derby-winning jockey Laffit Pincay Jr?

6   What nationality is Classic-winning jockey Andrea Atzeni?

7   What nationality was Cheltenham Gold Cup-winning jockey Adam Kondrat?

8   What nationality is three-times Kentucky Derby-winning jockey Angel Cordero Jr?

9   What nationality is dual Arc de Triomphe-winning jockey Christophe Soumillon?

10 What nationality is multiple Group 1-winning Flat jockey Adrie De Vries?

ROUND 82
IN THE PRESS ROOM

All the questions relate to racing media

1   Which racecourse commentator's daughter Eleanor starred as Demelza opposite Aidan Turner in the BBC's adaption of Poldark that was screened from 2015 to 2019?

2   Who in December 2018 succeeded Bruce Millington as editor of the Racing Post?

3   Alan Lee, The Times racing correspondent before his sudden death in 2015, had previously covered which sport for the same newspaper?

4   Long-time BBC commentator Sir Peter O'Sullevan was, for many years, also racing correspondent of which newspaper?

5   Colin Mackenzie, the one-time racing correspondent of the Daily Mail, when working as a news reporter tracked down which notorious criminal?

6   The Horserace Writers and Photographers Association hold an annual lunch on the first Monday of December with an annual awards ceremony that takes its name from the organisation's patron. What is it called?

7   At those awards in 2018, who won the Clive Graham Trophy, named after the HWPA's first president, for racing writer of the year for a record fifth time?

8   Which TV presenter is the nephew of a Derby-winning trainer?

9   By what name did charismatic betting pundit John McCririck regularly refer to his wife Jenny? He took the name from a type of sea bird.

10   What is the name of the self-styled social media character known as the Racing Blogger?

ROUND 83
NAME DROPPERS

All the answers or questions relate to horses with familiar first names

1 Who rode One For Arthur to victory in the 2017 Grand National?

2 Who trained Annie Power to win her first two bumper races?

3 Which jockey rode Anthony Van Dyck to victory in the 2019 Derby?

4 Sir Percy, winner of the 2006 Derby, had previously finished second behind which horse in the 2000 Guineas?

5 Which 100-1 shot was the only horse to complete the course without remounting when he won the 1928 Grand National?

6 Which horse gave John Gosden his first Derby winner?

7 Who owned the 2017 Cheltenham Gold Cup winner Sizing John?

8 Which mare won the Cleeve Hurdle three times for Venetia Williams and jockey Norman Williamson?

9 Which horse gave trainer Mark Tompkins his only Classic winner when landing the 1993 St Leger?

10 Which horse won the 1999 Welsh Grand National for trainer Henry Daly and jockey Richard Johnson?

ROUND 84
MR & MRS

The questions or answers all have horses with Mr, Mrs, Master or Miss contained in their names

1 Which horse beat Red Rum's track record when landing the 1990 Grand National on ground officially described as firm?

2 Which mare won the 1987 Liverpool Hurdle for the then permit trainer Nigel Twiston-Davies? He later named his house after her.

3 Which owner is reported to have bet £500,000 each-way on his horse, Mr Snugfit, in the 1986 Grand National?

4 Which subsequent Cheltenham Gold Cup winner was pulled up in a Newbury novices' chase on his 'rules' debut?

5 Mrs McArdy gave which trainer his only Classic winner when she landed the 1000 Guineas in 1977?

6 Which Australian sprinter won the 2007 King's Stand Stakes at Royal Ascot?

7 Which horse won the 1958 Grand National by 30 lengths despite his jockey Arthur Freeman putting up 6lbs overweight?

8 Which horse, named after an American actor, writer and director, put Lester Piggott in intensive care when he suffered a fatal fall in the 1992 Breeders' Cup Sprint?

9 Mister Donovan gave which owner his first Cheltenham Festival winner when he landed the race now known as the Ballymore Novices' Hurdle in 1982?

10 Which champion American stallion sired 1000 Guineas heroine Ravinella, Sussex Stakes winner Distant View and Kentucky Derby victor Fusaichi Pegasus?

ROUND 85
MASKED JOCKEYS

Identify the National Hunt jockeys in their Covid masks

Photos courtesy of focusonracing.com

ROUND 86
WHOSE ROUND IS IT ANYWAY?

All the questions relate to racecourse bars or restaurants

1   Which course turned its historic former weighing room into a bar called McCoy's?

2   At which track is course specialist Rapid Lad honoured with a bar named after him?

3   Which course has a bar named after dual Champion Hurdler Comedy Of Errors?

4   At which course would you be if you were having coffee in the Bramble Tudor Café?

5   Where would you be if you were drinking in the Chicken Hutch Bar?

6   At which racecourse is the Zetland Bar situated?

7   At which racecourse is the Tommy Atkins Bar one of the most popular watering holes?

8   At which racecourse would you be if you were having a drink in the Badger Bar?

9   At which racecourse could you dine in the Double Trigger Restaurant?

10   At which racecourse could you enjoy a drink on the Lester Piggott Roof Terrace?

ROUND 87
COURSES FOR HORSES

All the answers are British racecourses

1 On which racecourse would you find Swinley Bottom? It is 73ft lower than the winning post.

2 Which course hosted the Royal meeting while Ascot was being redeveloped in 2005?

3 Where was the first Sunday meeting in Britain held in 1992? It attracted a crowd of 23,000 despite no betting being allowed.

4 Which course is situated alongside the A1(M)? There is a young offenders prison almost opposite the track.

5 On the approach to which racecourse is there a set of roundabouts after which a Grade 1 chase is named?

6 Which racecourse closed in December 2012 but was reopened nearly four years later?

7 Which racecourse hands out world-renowned sticky toffee pudding as part of the winners' prize?

8 Which racecourse is unique in Britain in that it doesn't have a grandstand?

9 As of 2021, which current British racecourse also has a greyhound track on the same site?

10 At which racecourse can members of the public watch the action for free from the Roman city walls?

ROUND 88
TOP TEN

The answer to each question is a number from one to ten – each number is used only once

1   How many times was Richard Johnson champion jumps jockey?

2   How many Derby winners did Lester Piggott ride?

3   How many times did Red Rum win the Grand National?

4   How many furlongs is the distance of the Hungerford Stakes?

5   How many times did Kauto Star win the King George VI Chase at Kempton?

6   How many horses finished the 2001 Grand National without remounting?

7   What number fence is Becher's Brook on the first circuit of the Grand National course?

8   What number appears in the name of the winners of the Cheltenham Gold Cup in 1954 and 1975?

9   How many times did AP McCoy win the Grand National?

10   How many hurdles have to be jumped in two-mile hurdles races?

ROUND 89
DEFUNCT AND DERELICT

All the questions relate to racecourses closed since WWII

1   Which racecourse, situated on the banks of the River Thames near Hampton Court, had one of its stands transported to Mansfield Town Football Club when it closed in 1962?

2   Which racecourse, which held a replacement race for the Grand National during WWI, closed in 1948 and can be remembered by drinking in the Flying Horse pub where the track once stood?

3   Which racecourse, closed in 1970, was known as the 'frying pan' due to the shape of the track?

4   Which racecourse, closed in 1960, was home to the Dartmoor Chase? The original grandstand can still be seen and the course has since been revived as a point-to-point track.

5   Which racecourse was unique for having a main road (A57) pass between the track and the main grandstand? The road had to be closed on race days.

6   At which racecourse, now closed, did AP McCoy ride his 4,000th winner on Mountain Tunes in 2013?

7   Which racecourse, closed in 1981, is now the site of a housing estate and a shopping centre called Teeside Park?

8   Wye racecourse closed in 1975. In which county was it situated?

9   Which racecourse, closed in 1948, was situated on the banks of the River Usk near Caerleon?

10   Which racecourse, closed in 2012, was situated on the Westenhanger Estate, which dates back to the 11th century and was once owned by King Canute?

ROUND 90
A QUESTION OF SPORT

All the questions are related to other sports connected to racing

1   Where was the Greyhound Derby run in 2021?

2   Where was the Formula One British Grand Prix run five times between 1955 and 1962?

3   What is the only city in Britain to have a racecourse, Premier League football ground, County Cricket ground and Premiership rugby ground?

4   The Racecourse Ground is officially recognised as the oldest international football stadium still in use. Which club play their home games there?

5   The Dringhouses Bowls Club is situated within the stable yard of which racecourse?

6   Which county cricket club's ground, formerly known as the Racecourse Ground, was initially located inside the town's racecourse?

7   Which racecourse is located on an estate that also hosts the 'Festival of Speed'?

8   Bath, Hexham, Leicester, Kelso and Stratford are among more than a dozen racecourses used by the RPRA for which sport?

9   Town Moor Golf Club is situated in the middle of which racecourse?

10   Which British racecourse in 2014 served as the starting line for the Tour de France?

ROUND 91
FRANKIE'S MAGNIFICENT SEVEN

All the questions relate to Frankie Dettori's Magnificent Seven winners at Ascot in 1996

1 A pound accumulator on all seven winners would have returned how much money (to the nearest £1,000)?

2 Which horse, named after a feature of the financial district of New York, was the first winner on the card?

3 Diffident won the second race in what is now the British Champions Sprint. What was the race called in 1996?

4 Which Classic winner finished second to Frankie in the big race of the day, the Queen Elizabeth II Stakes?

5 The sixth leg was won by a filly who went on to land the Group 1 Nunthorpe Stakes two years later and was a half-sister of champion sprinter Lochsong, who Frankie also rode to win the Nunthorpe. Who was she?

6 On leaving the parade ring before the final race Frankie told his final winner's trainer "if this gets beaten it's your fault because I'm on fire". Who was the trainer?

ROUND 92
THE HIT PARADE

All the questions have a musical theme

1 Cockney Rebel, named after rocker Steve Harley's band, won the 2000 Guineas and Irish equivalent in 2007. Who trained him?

2 Which song by country favourite Glen Campbell gave its name to a horse who won what is now the Ultima Chase under AP McCoy at the 2009 Cheltenham Festival?

3 Which song, released in 1972, contains the line "well, I hear you went up to Saratoga and your horse naturally won"? It was a number one hit in America, Canada and Australia, and reached number three in the UK.

4 The title of the Bing Crosby song 'Where The Turf Meets The Surf' is taken from which racecourse's slogan? Crosby was a member of the partnership who built the track, which has hosted the Breeders' Cup.

5 Which long-standing owner, who was co-founder of Chrysalis Records, owned Culture Vulture, the first English-trained winner of the Poule d'Essai des Pouliches (French 1000 Guineas)?

6 Australian pop star Daryl Braithwaite traditionally sings his hit song 'The Horses' at Moonee Valley in front of the crowd before which race?

7 Which horse, named after an Eric Clapton song, won the Group 1 Qipco British Champions Fillies & Mares Stakes at Ascot on Champions Day in 2021?

8 Which amateur jockey rode Rhinestone Cowboy to win the 2004 Aintree Hurdle?

9 Which champion sprinter, named after a famous composer, won the July Cup and Nunthorpe Stakes in 2001?

10 Which filly, ridden by Walter Swinburn, gave Sir Michael Stoute his first victory in the 1000 Guineas in 1989?

ROUND 93
LOCATION, LOCATION, LOCATION

Identify the racecourse from clues connected to notable nearby landmarks

1   Which racecourse is situated nearest to the largest army garrison in Europe?

2   Which racecourse is situated nearest to Alton Towers theme park?

3   Which racecourse is situated nearest to a rugby stadium that was originally known as Billy Williams' Cabbage Patch?

4   Which National Hunt course is situated closest to the National Horseracing Museum?

5   Which racecourse is situated nearest to the southern-most point of Offa's Dyke?

6   Which racecourse is situated nearest to the Angel Of The North statue?

7   Which racecourse is situated nearest to Stonehenge?

8   Which racecourse is situated nearest to the National Railway Museum?

9   Which racecourse is situated nearest to Stanstead Airport?

10   Which racecourse is situated nearest to Scafell Pike?

ROUND 94
NICKNAMES

All the questions relate to nicknames given to racing personalities

1   Which dual champion apprentice jockey was known as the Angry Ant?

2   Which Cheltenham Gold Cup-winning jockey is known as Puppy?

3   Chris Grant was regarded as one of the toughest jump jockeys of the 1980s. What nickname was he given by his weighing room colleagues?

4   In a career spanning three decades Harry Wragg became famed for his come-from-behind style of race riding. What nickname was he given?

5   Which jockey rode ill-fated Golden Cygnet to a brilliant win in the 1978 Supreme Novices' Hurdle? He was known as Boots and his jockey sons followed the theme with Slippers and Socks.

6   Which British champion Flat jockey was known as the Kentucky Kid?

7   Which Group 1-winning Flat jockey – the son of a jockey-turned trainer – was known as Trotter? As a youngster he trotted after his dad at the races.

8   Which Cheltenham Gold Cup-winning jockey was known as Lens or Lensio as he needed contact lenses to be able to ride in races?

9   Which Classic-winning rider – now a TV presenter – is known as Shark?

10   Which jumps jockey was known as Chocolate or Choc for short? He was given the name by first boss David Nicholson as he appeared to eat nothing else.

ROUND 95
AHEAD OF THE GAME

Questions relating to racing firsts

1   Which was the first racecourse to stage a fixture behind closed doors due to the Covid-19 pandemic in 2021?

2   Who was the first jumps jockey to ride 1,000 winners?

3   Which contest is traditionally the first race of the Cheltenham Festival?

4   Who was the first female jockey to ride a winner at Royal Ascot?

5   Which horse was the first Derby winner decided by a photo-finish?

6   Which horse gave the Queen her first Classic winner?

7   Which horse won the first Champion Hurdle after World War II?

8   Which horse was the first British runner to finish the 2021 Grand National? In finishing sixth he was the only British-trained horse in the first 11 home.

9   Jenny Pitman became the first female trainer to win the Cheltenham Gold Cup when which horse was successful?

10 Which trainer was responsible for Plunkett, who won the first race at Ffos Las' opening meeting on 18 June 2009?

ROUND 96
THE CRYPTIC FACTOR

All the questions are rather cryptic – much like clues to some crossword puzzles

1 French writer Henri Charriere's nickname and most famous work won the 2000 Grand National.

2 The 1949 Grand National winner might well have been Yuri Gagarin, Yuri Zhivago or Ivan Susanin.

3 The 1967 Derby winner who could have been from Holyroodhouse or Sandringham.

4 The 2016 Cheltenham Gold cup winner who could have been a skilled horseman and an experienced warrior in Russia.

5 The 1991 Cheltenham Gold Cup winner has his very own racecourse in Barbados.

6 The 2004 Oaks winner would have used a planchette to spell out messages during a séance.

7 The most famous Grand National runner-up could be salt 'n' vinegar, smoky bacon or even just plain old ready salted.

8 The first of Barry Geraghty's four Champion Hurdle winners was from a region often known as the breadbasket of both Indian and Pakistan.

9 The winner of the 2016 King's Stand Stakes was a nice little earner for trainer Clive Cox and trainer Adam Kirby.

10 Frankie Dettori won his first Nunthorpe Stakes to the tune of music from a Scottish Lake.

GUESS WHO?

Identify the famous racing personalities

Photos courtesy of Bernard Parkin

ROUND 98
ON THE MAP

All the questions relate to towns, cities or countries

1 Which horse won his second Queen Mother Champion Chase at the of 11? He also won two Tingle Creek Chases.

2 Which horse won the Derby and Irish Derby in 2014?

3 Which St Leger winner, who went on to be a successful NH stallion, was beaten into second place in the 2001 Breeders' Cup Turf by Fantastic Light?

4 Which horse won a record four Irish Gold Cups for three different jockeys?

5 What was the name of the Queen's 1977 Oaks and St Leger heroine?

6 Which is the only British city that gives its name to a National and a Gold Cup?

7 Which horse won the American Triple Crown in 1977?

8 Which horse won the Betfair Chase three times (2017, 2018, 2020) at Haydock?

9 Which horse gave trainer Ferdy Murphy the first of his three Scottish Grand National wins?

10 Which racecourse hosts the North Yorkshire Grand National?

ROUND 99
RICHARD JOHNSON

1 Which trainer was I attached to when I first became a professional jockey?

2 I was runner-up behind AP McCoy in the jockeys' championship no fewer than 16 times. Behind which other jockey did I finish second in the race to be champion jockey?

3 On which horse did I win the Hennessy Gold Cup, Welsh National and Cheltenham Gold Cup?

4 My father-in-law Noel Chance trained which horse, ridden by me, to win the Cheltenham Gold Cup?

5 On which horse, owned by the current (2021) chairman of Cheltenham Racecourse, did I win the bet365 Gold Cup in 2008?

6 I hold the record for riding the most times in the Grand National without winning it? How many times did I ride in the race?

7 On which horse did I twice win the Glenfarclas Cross Country Chase at the Cheltenham Festival?

8 On which horse did I twice win the Irish Gold Cup?

9 On which grey horse did I win the 2003 Champion Hurdle?

10 Which horse gave me my first Cheltenham Festival winner when successful in 1999?

ROUND 100
HOLLIE DOYLE AND TOM MARQUAND

Hollie

1   On which horse did I win my first Group 1 race?

2   How many winners did I ride at Windsor on the last Saturday of August 2020?

3   Which trainer did I join as apprentice in 2014

4   I rode my first Group-race winner on Dame Malliot in the Princess Of Wales's Stakes at Newmarket in 2020. Who was her trainer?

5   In which position did I finish in the 2020 BBC Sports Personality of the Year Awards?

Tom

1   On which British-trained horse did I win the Group 1 Queen Elizabeth Stakes in Australia in 2020 and 2021?

2   Which horse gave me my first Group-race winner when we landed the Dick Poole Fillies Stakes at 40-1 in 2017?

3   Which horse did I ride to win the Group 1 July Cup at Newmarket in 2021?

4   I spent much of my childhood living within 10 miles of which racecourse?

5   My first British Classic victory came in which race?

ROUND 101
GARY WILTSHIRE

1   In bookmaking parlance what is a 'carpet' and what is 'double carpet'?

2   What was the name of the bogus bookie who stood on Derby Day at Epsom in 1997? He did a runner without paying out punters and was never tracked down.

3   Like most kids growing up in the 1950s and 60s I was first introduced to horse racing - and bookmaking when I priced them up - through a game which involved a long piece of green fabric and five metal horses which moved by turning a handle. It was better than it sounds! What was it called?

4   I might have been later known as 'The Belly from the Telly', but as a youngster I was pretty athletic and played football for Islington Schoolboys - where I was born - as well as London Schoolboys. I also had trials for which two professional clubs?

5   I went to Highbury Grove School and our great rivals then were Holloway School. Who was their coach? He was a legendary Arsenal goalkeeper.

6   As a Londoner I made a book at most of the major greyhound tracks, now sadly closed as the price of land increased. One of the most famous was on the Chingford Road at the Crooked Billet roundabout. It was famous and iconic for its neon frontage and adjoining nightclub Charlie Chan's. What was it known as?

7   If I laid an 'even pony' - how much would the punter be wagering?

8   I spent many years making a book on the point-to-point circuit - and still do on occasions. Back in the day Ian Balding was the trainer to follow - or duck if you were a bookmaker – as his horses always seemed to win. Name his famous racehorse trainer brother, now sadly no longer with us, his famous racehorse trainer son and his famous TV-presenting daughter.

9   I've been lucky enough to own many greyhounds and horses over the years with a number of trainers, some sadly no longer with us. Give me the surnames of these two racehorse trainers I enjoyed success with: David W..... and Norma M.......?

10   Frankie Dettori went through the card at Ascot on September 28, 1996 - it's a day I remember well! But what was the name of the horse who completed Frankie's 'Magnificent Seven'?

JONATHAN HOBBS

1   Name the short-sighted greyhound made famous in the British sitcom Steptoe and Son Ride Again?

2   Romford was the scene of the first televised triple dead-heat in greyhound racing. Which three greyhounds dead-heated at the Essex track live on Sky Sports on January 19, 2011?

3   Name the four greyhounds to have won back-to-back Greyhound Derbys?

4   Which member of the Royal Family won the Greyhound Derby at White City with a greyhound by the name of Camira Flash in 1968?

5   Which member of the Royal Family owned 1990 Greyhound Derby runner-up Druids Johno?

6   London greyhound tracks White City and Wimbledon staged the Greyhound Derby for many years. During the Second World War which other venue in the capital hosted the famous event?

7   Broadcast as part of the BBC's midweek Sportsnight programme with commentary from the likes of David Coleman, Harry Carpenter and Gerald Sinstadt, where and in what year was the first BBC Television Trophy run?

8   Ballyregan Bob was one of the sport's biggest stars. His major claim to fame was breaking the-then world record of consecutive victories - a race at the Brighton & Hove Stadium which was broadcast live on the BBC's Nine O'Clock News on December 9, 1986. How long was his winning sequence?

9   Scurlogue Champ, a freak of a greyhound known for his whirlwind finishes, joined Ballyregan Bob in the John Power Showdown at Wembley in 1986. It was the first and only time these two giants of the track met - and the race attracted a huge crowd. However, it proved an anti-climax as 'The Champ' stopped chasing. But who were the other two greyhounds in the Showdown line-up?

10   Westmead Hawk was a greyhound so famous he was immortalised where?

ANSWERS

All answers have been researched as correct as at 1st September 2021.

1 AP McCoy

1. Toby Balding, 2. Jim Bolger, 3. Sir Gordon Richards, 4. Richard Dunwoody, 5. Blowing Wind, 6. Synchronised, 7. Arsenal, 8. Ray Parlour, 9. Unsinkable Boxer, 10. Make A Stand

2 Cornelius Lysaght

1. Peter Scudamore, 2. Nigel Twiston-Davies, 3. Charlie Brooks, 4. Michael Bowlby , 5. Barona, 6. Peter Bromley, 7. Shergar, 8. Make A Stand, 9. Rugby Union, 10. Cambridge

3 Paul Nicholls

1. Playschool, 2. David Barons, 3. Seagram, 4. 1999, 5. Cyborgo, 6. Kauto Star, 7. Wincanton, 8. Sam Thomas, 9. Queen Mother Champion Chase, 10. Ruby Walsh

4 Clare Balding

1. Willie Carson, 2. Frankel, 3. Casual Look/Martin Dwyer, 4. Champagne, 5. AP McCoy, 6. Frankie Dettori and Hollie Doyle, 7. Lord Gyllene, 8. Racehorse Who Wouldn't Gallop, 9. Emily Wilding Davison/Anmer, 10. Get Back On, Keep Going

5 Green Fingers

1. Ripon, 2. Capability Brown, 3. Rhododendron, 4. Kentucky Derby, 5. Monet's Garden, 6. Snowdrop, 7. Queen's Vase, 8. Cottage Rake, 9. Honeysuckle , 10. Iris's Gift

6 Masked Flat Jockeys

1. Adam Kirby, 2. Andrea Atzeni, 3. Frankie Dettori, 4. Hayley Turner, 5. Nicola Currie, 6. Rab Havlin, 7. Silvestre de Sousa, 8. Tom Queally

7 Keep It In The Family

1. Macer and Josh Gifford, 2. Martin and Tim Malony, 3. Jose and Irad Ortiz, 4. Frankel, 5. Morley Street and Granville Again, 6. Katie Walsh, 7. Ryan Moore, 8. Doug and Eph Smith, 9. Denman, 10. Michael and Richard Hills

8 Seeing Is Believing

1. Trelawny, 2. Champion Hurdle, 3. Mme Hennessy, 4. Aidan O'Brien, 5. The Queen, 6. Willie Robinson, 7. The result was a dead-heat with Coastal Bluff, 8. Arkle and Mill House , 9. Chaplins Club, 10. It came on the same day Prince William and Kate Middleton got married

9 Culture Vultures

1. Brigadier Gerard, 2. Charles W Engelhard Jr, 3. Mahler, 4. Dylan Thomas, 5. The Great Gatsby, 6. Comedy Of Errors, 7. Riverside Theatre, 8. Roderic O'Connor, 9. Debussy, 10. Golden Fleece

10 Red Rum's Third Grand National Victory

1. Southport, 2. Churchtown Boy, 3. Red Alligator, 4. L'Escargot, 5. Charlotte Brew, 6. Lee Mack

11 The Female Of The Species

1. David Nicholson, 2. Gallows. Infamous highwayman Dick Turpin was one of those hanged there. 3. Dawn Run, 4. Oh So Sharp, 5. Nell Gwyn Stakes, 6. Love, 7. Soviet Song, 8. Hatoof, 9. George Duffield, 10. Nickel Coin

12 Colour Coded

1. Silver Birch, 2. Whiteoak, 3. Black Caviar, 4. Blue Peter, 5. Red Evie, 6. Blue Bunting, 7. Russe Blanc, 8. Paul Green, 9. Blue (Blue Judge and Blues Traveller), 10. Big Orange

13 Drinks Cabinet

1. Schweppes Gold Trophy, 2. Denman, 3. Seagram, 4. Night Nurse, 5. Guinness, 6. Doncaster, 7. Cider With Rosie, 8. Mackeson, 9. Budweiser, 10. Pisco Sour

14 Landed Gentry

1. Lord John Oaksey, 2. Sir Percy, 3. Best Mate, 4. Lord Vestey, 5. Lord Windermere, 6. Duke Of Richmond and Gordon (Lord March), 7. Barry Hills, 8. Baron Windrush, 9. Services to tourism in Barbados, 10. Lord Derby

15 2021

1. Seeyouatmidnight, 2. Denise Foster, 3. None, 4. Minella Times, 5. John Leeper, 6. St Mark's Basilica, 7. Jim Goldie, 8. Oisin Murphy, 9. Marco Ghiani, 10. Barry Hearn

16 Land Of My Fathers

1. Coral, 2. Carl Llewellyn, 3. Ffos Las, 4. Tregaron, 5. Geoff Lewis, 6. Peter Bowen, 7. The Tatling, 8. Sirrell Griffiths, 9. Flintshire, 10. Tenby

17 Match The Name

1. D - Andy Pandy, 2. F - Giants Causeway , 3. A - The Thinker, 4. E - Camelot , 5. H - Rip Van Winkle, 6. C - Santa Claus, 7. B - Ben Nevis, 8. G - Anthony Van Dyck

18 The Long And The Short Of It

1. Eight, 2. Nose, 3. The Chair, 4. Pontefract, 5. Chester, 6. Four, 7. 510 miles, 8. 5ft 8ins (1.73m), 9. Bath, 10. Epsom

19 Around The Tracks

1. Cartmel, 2. Epsom, 3. Chepstow, 4. Galway, 5. Perth, 6. Ludlow, 7. York, 8. Uttoxeter, 9. Newmarket, 10. Worcester

20 Close But No Cigar

1. Walkon, 2. Desert Orchid, 3. Sausalito Bay, 4. Excelebration, 5. 16, 6. Davy Jones, 7. Glint of Gold, 8. Greville Starkey, 9. Dee Ex Bee, 10. Hawk Wing

21 Money Matters

1. £3,150, 2. Riyadh, 3. Whitbread, 4. Qipco, 5. Ever Ready, 6. Cash Asmussen, 7. Darren Yates, 8. Magners, 9. £85,000, 10. Daily Telegraph

22 Family Connections

1. Hywel Davies – H James Davies, 2. Tommy Kinane – D Mick Kinane, 3. Frenchie Nicholson – B David Nicholson, 4. Dessie Hughes – C Richard Hughes, 5. Gianfranco Dettori – G Frankie Dettori, 6. Jamie Osborne – A Saffie Osborne, 7. Jonjo O'Neill - I Jonjo O'Neill Jnr, 8. Jimmy Frost – F Bryony Frost, 9. Kieren Fallon – E Cieren Fallon

23 Frankie Dettori

1. Sir Henry Cecil, 2. Balanchine, 3. July Cup, 4. Luca Cumani, 5. Arsenal, 6. Mark Of Esteem, 7. Dubai Millennium, 8. Ally McCoist, 9. 11, 10. Stradivarius

24 Nick Luck

1. It held the first Sunday UK race meeting with legal betting, 2. Shangamuzo, 3. Clive Smith (Kauto Star), 4. Ruling Dynasty, 5. Tom Grantham, 6. Cash Asmussen, 7. Patrick Byrne, 8. Nottingham, 9. Howard Johnson and Graham Lee, 10. She foaled on 21 Dec meaning her filly foal, later named Liel, could not have any meaningful racing career

25 John Francome

1. Multigrey, 2. David Coleman, 3. Bill Shoemark, 4. Lanzarote, 5. Fulke Walwyn, 6. Duke of Alburquerque, 7. The race was run in April after snow caused the original fixture to be cancelled, 8. Grand National, Cheltenham Gold Cup, Champion Hurdle, 9. Sonny Somers, 10. Phil Tuck

26 Brough Scott

1. Warrior, 2. John, 3. Ian Fleming, 4. Lingfield, 5. ITV , 6. It finished last at Cheltenham, 7. Red Rum, 8. Ian Botham , 9. He wouldn't talk to me, 10. Deep freeze

27 The Sky's The Limit

1. Sun Princess, 2. Many Clouds, 3. Moonax, 4. Rainbow Quest, 5. Sea The Stars, 6. Sky Lantern, 7. Foxhunters' Chase, 8. John Dunlop, 9. Lucinda Russell, 10. Lightning Spear

28 The Suffragette Derby

1. King George V, 2. Women's Social and Political Union, 3. Emmeline Pankhurst, 4. White Star Line, 5. 100-1, 6. American

29 What's In A Name

1. Frenchie Nicholson, 2. The Duke, 3. Henry, 4. John Dunlop, 5. Walsh (Ruby and Mark), 6. Peter, 7. Fred Archer, 8. Claude Duval (The Sun), 9. Walter Swinburn, 10. William Hastings-Bass (Lord Huntingdon)

30 Feathered Friends

1. Indian Skimmer, 2. Darren Bird, 3. Rooster Booster, 4. Sir David Robinson, 5. Charlie Swan, 6. Bullfinch, 7. Jim Wilson, 8. Flakey Dove, 9. Monksfield, 10. Rock Hopper

31 In The Beginning

1. Charles II, 2. Queen Anne, 3. Jockey Club, 4. Yorkshire, 5. The Carlisle Bell, 6. The Sporting Life, 7. Sir Charles Bunbury, 8. Eclipse, 9. Tod Sloan, 10. Chester

32 Stars And Stripes

1. The Preakness Stakes, 2. Jay Trump, 3. Bill Shoemaker, 4. Cash Asmussen, 5. Jonathan Sheppard, 6. Louisville, 7. Lonesome Glory, 8. Cigar, 9. Tepin, 10. Hollywood Park

33 Masked Jumps Trainers

1. Jonjo O'Neill, 2. Dan Skelton, 3. Emma Lavelle, 4. Henry de Bromhead, 5. Henry Daly, 6. Jamie Snowden , 7. Noel Meade, 8. Paul Nicholls

34 Rank Outsider

1. 300-1, 2. Mon Mome, 3. Padraig Beggy, 4. Coventry Stakes, 5. Cieren Fallon, 6. Terimon, 7. Graham McCourt, 8. Jim Bolger, 9. Beech Road, 10. David Elsworth

35 Football Crazy

1. Sunderland, 2. Peter Shilton, 3. Franny Lee, 4. Samitar, 5. Jamesmead, 6. Seebald, 7. Brown Panther, 8. Glen Johnson, 9. Seven, 10. Kevin Keegan

36 Grey Days

1. Senor El Betrutti, 2. One Man, 3. Daryl Jacob, 4. Newmarket, 5. Daylami, 6. Native Dancer, 7. Brighton, 8. Nicolaus Silver, 9. The Grey Gatsby, 10. Silver Patriarch

37 What's On The Menu?

1. Beef Or Salmon, 2. Oxo, 3. Graham Roach, 4. Melon, 5. Cold Turkey, 6. Seafood, 7. Ginger Nut, 8. Brown Windsor, 9. Rogan Josh , 10. Caspian Caviar

38 Racecourse Layouts

1. Beverley, 2. Chester, 3. Epsom, 4. Goodwood, 5. Hamilton, 6. Newmarket (Rowley Mile), 7. Ripon, 8. Brighton

39 Those Who Pay The Bills

1. Sheikh Mohammed, 2. Ronnie and Reggie Kray, 3. Tractors, 4. John Hales (Neptune Collonges), 5. Raymond Guest, 6. Daniel Wildenstein, 7. William Haggas (Christine Feather), 8. Cool Dawn, 9. Persian War, 10. Bill Gredley

40 Scandal And Skullduggery

1. Gay Future, 2. Kieren Fallon, 3. David Nicholson, 4. Encke, 5. Terry Ramsden, 6. Jamie Osborne, 7. Ile De Chypre, 8. Luke Harvey, 9. Graham Bradley, 10. Nipper Read

41 Tartan Army

1. Lucinda Russell, 2. Lucy Alexander, 3. Musselburgh, 4. Iain Jardine , 5. York, 6. John Douglas, 7. Golden Cygnet, 8. Willie Carson, 9. Hamilton Park, 10. Aberdeen

42 Stable Life

1. Sir Mark Prescott, 2. David Pipe, 3. Mark Johnston, 4. Philip Hobbs, 5. John and Thady Gosden, 6. Fergal O'Brien, 7. Nicky Henderson, 8. Nigel Twiston-Davies, 9. Richard Fahey, 10. Michael Bell

43 The Number Board

1. 30, 2. 59, 3. 40, 4. 12, 5. 75, 6. Five (Ayr, Hamilton, Kelso, Musselburgh, Perth), 7. Five, 8. 26, 9. 10, 10. 22

44 Guess Who

1. Princess Anne, 2. Clare Balding, 3. Jamie Spencer , 4. Woodrow Wyatt, 5. Norman Williamson, 6. Jim Bolger, 7. Edward O'Grady, 8. AP McCoy, 9. Edward Gillespie

45 Screen Stars

1. Silver Blaze, 2. Trainer, 3. Handsome Samson, 4. Edward Woodward, 5. Welsh National, 6. Seabiscuit, 7. Ealing Studios, 8. Nick Luck, 9. Melbourne Cup, 10. George Formby

46 On The Trot

1. Stradivarius, 2. Quevega, 3. Big Buck's, 4. Brown Jack, 5. Theatreworld , 6. Yeats, 7. Golden Miller, 8. Further Flight, 9. Winx, 10. David Probert

47 Odds Compilers

1. 11, 2. It's an outsider, 3. £500, 4. Heinz, 5. Burlington Bertie, 6. Scoop6, 7. Betfred, 8. BAGS (bookmakers' afternoon greyhound service), 9. 9-4, 10. Paris-mutuel

48 History Lesson

1. Galileo, 2. Persian War, 3. The Tetrarch, 4. Watling Street, 5. Camelot, 6. George Washington, 7. Henrythenavigator, 8. Rodrigo De Triano, 9. Brian Boru, 10. Aristotle

49 Shergar Kidnapped

1. Chester Vase, 2. Lester Piggott, 3. Ballymany Stud, 4. It was the codeword given by the kidnappers to identify them in subsequent phone calls, 5. Derek Thompson, 6. Goodwood

50 It's A Colourful Life

1. Winston Churchill, 2. Barney Curley, 3. Dorothy Paget, 4. Sir Alex Ferguson, 5. Ronnie Wood, 6. Robbie Fowler and Steve McManaman, 7. Million In Mind Partnership, 8. Chesney Allen, 9. Harry Redknapp, 10. Benny Andersson (ABBA)

51 Peter Scudamore

1. Davy Jones, 2. Bonanza Boy, 3. Reg Hollinshead, 4. He was trained by my grandfather Geoff, 5. Ladbrokes Trophy (formerly the Hennessy Gold Cup) , 6. Rose Park (dad), Thistlecrack (Tom), 7. Ryan Moore, 8. Paul Carberry, 9. The English Premier League, 10. Huntingdon

52 Ryan Moore

1. Brighton and Hove Albion, 2. Richard Hannon, 3. Notnowcato, 4. Workforce, 5. The Queen, 6. The Melbourne Cup, 7. St Leger, 8. Conduit, 9. Ed Dunlop, 10. Sire De Grugy

53 Luke Harvey

1. Captain Tim Forster, 2. Jim Wilson, 3. Paul Holley, 4. He was the first horse I trained to win a point-to-point, 5. Mark Richards, 6. Fit To Ride, 7. Solidasarock, 8. Reg Akehurst, 9. Jason Weaver, 10. Cleeve Hill

54 David Yates

1. Huntingdon, 2. Fergal Lynch, 3. 13, 4. 2004, 5. Camphor, 6. Musselburgh, 7. Six (Royal Ascot and Derby day), 8. Adrian Maguire, 9. Shaamit (1996), 10. Mick Kinane

55 Set Your SatNav

1. Haydock Park, 2. Chepstow, 3. Uttoxeter, 4. Ayr, 5. Wetherby, 6. Fakenham, 7. Wincanton, 8. Bangor-on-Dee, 9. Ludlow, 10. Thirsk

56 Racing Golfers

1. Carl Llewellyn, 2. John Francome, 3. AP McCoy, 4. Clare Balding, 5. JP McManus, 6. Richard Hughes, 7. David Pipe, 8. Oliver Sherwood

57 The Greatest

1. John Francome, 2. Leicester, 3. Don't Push It, 4. John Kempton, 5. Stayers' Hurdle, 6. Nicky Henderson, 7. William Haggas, 8. Trempolino, 9. Nathaniel, 10. Andrea Atzeni

58 Trophy Hunters

1. Wincanton, 2. York, 3. Exeter, 4. Salisbury, 5. Goodwood, 6. Ffos Las, 7. Chester, 8. Huntingdon, 9. Lingfield, 10. Sandown

59 Aussie Rules

1. Randwick, 2. Scobie Breasley, 3. Aussie Rules, 4. Bart Cummings, 5. Black Caviar, 6. Melbourne, 7. True (more than 360!), 8. Perth, 9. Jim McGrath, 10. Melbourne Cup

60 At The Bar

1. Amato, 2. Jonjo O'Neill, 3. Manor House Inn, 4. The Hollow Bottom, 5. Luke Harvey, 6. York,
7. Newmarket, 8. Kempton Park, 9. John Smith's, 10. Fred Archer

61 Racecourse Layouts

1. Cartmel, 2. Cheltenham, 3. Exeter, 4. Fakenham, 5. Fontwell, 6. Perth, 7. Stratford, 8. Uttoxeter

62 Jockeys' Board

1. Lord Oaksey, 2. Mark Hely-Hutchinson, 3. Minette Batters, 4. Peter Scudamore (business
partner Nigel Twiston-Davies and Lucinda Russell), 5. Willie Carson, 6. Guy Disney, 7. Ian Balding,
8. Michael Dickinson, 9. Sam Waley-Cohen , 10. Richard Dunwoody

63 Better Breeding

1. Dorothy Paget , 2. Shadwell Estate, 3. Qatar Racing, 4. Cheveley Park Stud, 5. 13, 6. Thunder
And Roses, 7. Tim Vigors, 8. Godolphin, 9. Juddmonte, 10. Newmarket July Course

64 Stewards Enquiry

1. Tied Cottage, 2. Jacqueline's Quest, 3. Mars bars, 4. Cahervillahow, 5. Be My Royal, 6. Royal Gait,
7. The Aga Khan, 8. Gold Cup at Royal Ascot, 9. After the race she was found to be year-older
stablemate Millie's Kiss, 10. Simple Verse

65 Tipping Line

1. Templegate, 2. Prince Monolulu, 3. Daily Mail, 4. Bouverie, 5. Pricewise, 6. David Ashforth,
7. Andy Beyer, 8. Daily Telegraph, 9. The Sporting Life, 10. Newsboy

66 Masked Flat Trainers

1. Charlie Hills, 2. Gay Kellaway, 3. George Boughey, 4. John Gosden, 5. Andrew Balding, 6. Marcus
Tregoning, 7. Mark Johnston, 8. Tim Easterby

67 Luck Of The Irish

1. Tommy Carberry, 2. Arkle, 3. Fortria, 4. Desert King, 5. Hurricane Fly, 6. Leopardstown,
7. Vintage Crop, 8. Vinnie Roe, 9. Vincent O'Brien, 10. Ruby Walsh

68 Life Beneath The Waves

1. Sea Bird, 2. Seabass, 3. Ocean Swell, 4. Fontwell, 5. Seabiscuit, 6. David Bass, 7. Pearl Diver,
8. 127, 9. Deano's Beano, 10. Mediterranean

69 The Smiths

1. John Smith's, 2. Tommy Smith, 3. Farrier, 4. Denys Smith, 5. Steve Smith Eccles, 6. Smith's
Lawn, 7. Clive Smith, 8. Derrick Smith, 9. Sue Smith, 10. Handicapper

70 For The Love Of It

1. Patrick Mullins, 2. Marcus Amytage, 3. Sam Waley-Cohen, 4. John Lawrence (Lord Oaksey),
5. Carruthers, 6. Gee Armytage, 7. Venetia Williams, 8. Caroline Beasley, 9. Prince Charles,
10. Jim Wilson

71 Racing Around The World

1. Australia, 2. Barbados, 3. New Zealand, 4. South Africa, 5. Japan, 6. Hungary, 7. Hong Kong,
8. Czech Republic, 9. Kenya, 10. India

72 Devon Loch Grand National Mystery

1. ESB, 2. Dave Dick, 3. The Queen Mother, 4. Kent, 5. Dead Cert, 6. Sunday Express

73 Jonjo O'Neill

1. Joseph, 2. Dawn Run, 3. Glencaraig Lady, 4. Queen Alexandra Stakes, 5. Reach at least 100
winners in a season, 6. Sea Pigeon, 7. Cartmel, 8. John Francome, 9. Switzerland, 10. Jackdaw's
Castle

74 Richard Hoiles

1. Pegwell Bay, 2. Stanmore (Stan Moore), 3. Fontwell, 4. Run For Free, Riverside Boy, Miinnehoma,
Bonanza Boy, 5. Pilsudski (Walter Swinburn and Mick Kinane), 6. Johan Cruyff, 7. Fernando Jara
and Invasor, 8. Silent Witness, 9. Moore, Powell and Murphy, 10. Craig Kieswetter

75 David Pipe

1. Freddie Starr, 2. Bookmaker, 3. Peter and Tom Scudamore, 4. My dad Martin, 5. Len Lungo, 6. Hopscotch, 7. Ryan Moore, 8. Junior, 9. Paul Nicholls, 10. Adrian Maguire

76 Ed Chamberlin

1. They arrived at the track very late, 2. Alice Plunkett, 3. Gordon Banks, 4. Her husband's ashes, 5. Oli Bell, 6. 13, 7. Luke Morris (Nunthorpe Stakes), 8. Southwell , 9. Royal Mail, 10. Lady Bowthorpe

77 This Is Your Life

1. Richard Johnson, 2. Timmy Murphy, 3. Barry Geraghty, 4. Jenny Pitman, 5. Lord John Oaksey, 6. Richard Dunwoody, 7. Sir Peter O'Sullevan, 8. Ginger McCain, 9. Graham Bradley, 10. Barney Curley

78 Vive La France

1. Deauville, 2. Bois de Boulogne, 3. Andre Fabre, 4. The French Furze, 5. The Fellow, 6. Mandarin, 7. Chantilly, 8. French Holly, 9. Jair Du Cochet, 10. Nupsala

79 Family Connections

1. Michael Scudamore – H Peter Scudamore , 2. Paddy Mullins – F Tony, Tom, Willie Mullins , 3. Nigel Twiston-Davies – G Sam Twiston-Davies, 4. Paul Nicholls – B Megan Nicholls, 5. Peter Scudamore – A Tom Scudamore , 6. Matt Sheppard – D Stan Sheppard , 7. Fergal O'Brien – I Fern O'Brien , 8. John Dunlop – C Ed Dunlop, 9. Luca Cumani – E Francesca Cumani

80 The Old Enemy

1. Victor Chandler, 2. Freddie Williams, 3. Denise Coates, 4. Barry Dennis (Bismarck), 5. Paddy Power, 6. John Banks, 7. Joe Coral, 8. Ladbrokes, 9. The Sun (Sunbets) , 10. The Asparagus Kid

81 Riding Around The Globe

1. South African, 2. Mexican, 3. Japanese, 4. Australian, 5. Panamanian , 6. Italian, 7. Polish, 8. Puerto Rican, 9. Belgian, 10. Dutch

82 In The Press Room

1. Malcolm Tomlinson, 2. Tom Kerr, 3. Cricket, 4. Daily Express , 5. Ronnie Biggs, 6. The Derby Awards, 7. Alastair Down, 8. Oli Bell, 9. The Booby , 10. Stephen Power

83 Name Droppers

1. Derek Fox, 2. Jim Bolger, 3. Seamie Heffernan, 4. George Washington, 5. Tipperary Tim, 6. Benny The Dip, 7. Ann and Alan Potts, 8. Lady Rebecca, 9. Bob's Return, 10. Edmond

84 Mr & Mrs

1. Mr Frisk, 2. Mrs Muck, 3. Terry Ramsden, 4. Master Oats, 5. Mick Easterby, 6. Miss Andretti, 7. Mr What, 8. Mr Brooks, 9. JP McManus, 10. Mr Prospector

85 Masked Jump Jockeys

1. Daryl Jacob, 2. David Bass, 3. Harry Cobden, 4. Nico de Boinville, 5. Robbie Dunne, 6. Sam Twiston-Davies, 7. Bryony Frost, 8. Paddy Brennan

86 Whose Round Is It Anyway?

1. Aintree, 2. Beverley, 3. Fontwell, 4. Hexham, 5. Kelso, 6. Redcar, 7. Cheltenham, 8. Wincanton, 9. Goodwood, 10. Salisbury

87 Courses For Horses

1. Ascot, 2. York, 3. Doncaster, 4. Wetherby, 5. Sandown (Scilly Isles Novices' Chase) , 6. Hereford, 7. Cartmel, 8. Bangor-on-Dee, 9. Nottingham, 10. Chester

88 Top Ten

1. Four, 2. Nine, 3. Three, 4. Seven, 5. Five, 6. Two, 7. Six, 8. Ten (Four Ten and Ten Up), 9. Once, 10. Eight

89 Defunct And Derelict

1. Hurst Park, 2. Gatwick, 3. Alexandra Park, 4. Buckfastleigh, 5. Lincoln, 6. Towcester, 7. Stockton, 8. Kent (between Ashford and Canterbury), 9. Newport, 10. Folkestone

90 A Question Of Sport

1. Towcester, 2. Aintree, 3. Leicester, 4. Wrexham, 5. York, 6. Derbyshire, 7. Goodwood,
8. Pigeon racing liberation sites (Royal Pigeon Racing Association), 9. Doncaster, 10. York

91 Frankie's Magnificent Seven

1. £25,095.50, 2. Wall Street, 3. Diadem Stakes, 4. Bosra Sham, 5. Lochangel, 6. Sir Michael Stoute

92 The Hit Parade

1. Geoff Huffer, 2. Wichita Lineman, 3. You're So Vain (Carly Simon), 4. Del Mar, 5. Chris Wright,
6. Cox Plate, 7. Wonderful Tonight, 8. JP Magnier, 9. Mozart, 10. Musical Bliss

93 Location, Location, Location

1. Catterick, 2. Uttoxeter, 3. Kempton Park (Twickenham), 4. Huntingdon, 5. Chepstow,
6. Newcastle, 7. Salisbury, 8. York, 9. Chelmsford, 10. Cartmel

94 Nicknames

1. Gary Bardwell, 2. Robbie Power, 3. Rambo, 4. The Head Waiter, 5. Niall Madden, 6. Steve
Cauthen, 7. Adrian Nicholls, 8. Andrew Thornton, 9. Jason Weaver, 10. Robert Thornton

95 Ahead Of The Game

1. Kelso, 2. Stan Mellor, 3. Supreme Novices' Hurdle, 4. Gay Kellaway, 5. Nimbus, 6. Carrozza,
7. Brains Trust, 8. Blaklion, 9. Burrough Hill Lad, 10. Evan Williams

96 The Cryptic Factor

1. Papillon, 2. Russian Hero, 3. Royal Palace, 4. Don Cossack, 5. Garrison Savannah, 6. Ouija Board,
7. Crisp, 8. Punjabi, 9. Profitable, 10. Lochsong

97 Guess Who?

1. Vincent O'Brien, 2. Ventia Williams, 3. Graham Bradley, 4. Fred Winter & Fred Rimell, 5. Olivier
Peslier , 6. John Francome , 7. Alastair Down, 8. Bob Champion, 9. Paddy Power

98 On The Map

1. Moscow Flyer, 2. Australia, 3. Milan, 4. Florida Pearl, 5. Dunfermline, 6. London (hosted by
Sandown and Newbury), 7. Seattle Slew, 8. Bristol De Mai, 9. Paris Pike, 10. Catterick

99 Richard Johnson

1. David Nicholson, 2. Brian Hughes, 3. Native River, 4. Looks Like Trouble, 5. Monkerhostin, 6. 21,
7. Balthazar King, 8. Florida Pearl, 9. Rooster Booster, 10. Anzum (Stayers' Hurdle)

100 Hollie Doyle and Tom Marquand

Hollie - 1. Glen Shiel, 2. Five, 3. Richard Hannon, 4. Ed Vaughan, 5. Third,
Tom - 1. Addeybb, 2. Anna Nerium, 3. Starman, 4. Cheltenham, 5. St Leger (Galileo Chrome)

101 Gary Wiltshire

1. 3-1. and 33-1, 2. John Batten, 3. Escalado, 4. Arsenal and Leyton Orient , 5. Bob Wilson, 6. The Stow
(or Walthamstow), 7. £25, 8. Toby, Andrew and Clare, 9. Wintle and Macauley, 10. Fujiyama Crest

102 Jonathan Hobbs

1. Hercules The Second, 2. Droopys Djokovic, Ayamzagirl and Killishin Masai, 3. Mick the Miller
(1929/30), Patricias Hope (1972/73), Rapid Ranger (2000/01) and Westmead Hawk (2005/06),
4. Prince Philip, 5. Prince Edward, 6. Harringay (1940), 7. Wimbledon in 1958, 8. 32 races,
9. Glenowen Queen and Track Man, 10. In Madame Tussauds alongside David Beckham, among
others. Beckham himself was a former 'potboy' at Walthamstow greyhound track, collecting beer
glasses as a 14-year-old for £2-an-hour.

INSIDE INFORMATION

Bresbet / Chris Coley

BRESBET, the UK's newest bookmaker, is delighted to be supporting the latest in a series of lockdown-inspired quiz books published by Chris Coley.

Chris is a well-known and popular figure in National Hunt racing and BresBet shares his love of horses and horse racing - with Ravenswell Farm very much at the heart of that being the home of trainer Fergal O'Brien and jockey – and BresBet Legend - Paddy Brennan.

Nic Brereton, chairman of BresBet, said: "Chris is a great supporter of Fergal's team and is one of the best-known names in jumps racing, so when he came to us with an offer to support him it was a no-brainer.

"We've been owners with Fergal for a few years now and have got to know Chris well – his passion for the sport and horses in general shines through.

"These books have been a labour of love for Chris and his broad knowledge of sport is clear to see. His efforts have been well received in lockdown - when we all had plenty more time for his quizzes!

"However, this publication is unique in that some well-known names have contributed - each asked to provide questions about themselves. We are proud therefore to include our own Gary Wiltshire here.

"Gary has enjoyed a colourful life and is still one of the most recognisable faces on the racecourse. Having Gary representing BresBet on-course has been huge in terms of cutting through and is a partnership we are looking forward to growing.

"We are also looking to establish the BresBet Foundation and are delighted that some of the proceeds of this book will support several charities we are involved with - including the Injured Jockeys Fund and horse and greyhound welfare charities."

Sheffield-based BresBet has a 'Back to Bookmaking' ethos and will be a punter-friendly presence across multiple platforms.

Dave Perry, BresBet's managing director, said: "We aim to make BresBet a force in a competitive market - online, on-course and retail.

"BresBet's pledge to its customers is one of loyalty, with a back-to-basics approach to bookmaking. This means taking a view and offering our customers something they are failing to get elsewhere. We aim to stand out from the crowd and to make it fun.

"In all of this, however, we will ensure we support the BresBet Foundation and its charitable partners. We are committed to giving something back, BresBet will be at the forefront of that."

Steve Jones

Lockdown affected us in many different ways. It left freelance journalist and broadcaster Steve Jones with plenty of time on his hands as racing shut down for the best part of three months.

Luckily, Chris Coley spun the idea of a racing quiz book in his direction and, suddenly, he didn't have to worry so much about how he was going to kill time.

Researching the book brought back many happy memories of trips to the races as first a wide-eyed teenager, then an enthusiastic punter, through to national newspaper tipster and writer.

These days he can be seen as a pundit for Racing TV, his tips appear every Saturday in the Daily Mirror and he writes big-race previews for Valuerater.co.uk.

Coming from a family of jockeys, Steve has been surrounded by racing his whole life and he knows full well the superb work carried out by the Injured Jockeys Fund.

His grandfather, Davy, rode Red Rower to win the 1945 Cheltenham Gold Cup when he was, supposedly, in the veteran stage for a jockey. Having switched to the Flat, riding as a lightweight, he continued to ride for more than another 25 years and he was 63 when he rode the winner of the Kenyan Derby.

Steve's father Peter rode the winner of the Cheltenham Festival's Grand Annual Chase and the Molyneux Chase over the Grand National fences. His uncle Buck, who rode primarily for Ryan Price, enjoyed his biggest win in the saddle in the Imperial Cup before taking up training.

Steve harboured ambitions to follow the family tradition but his dreams were held back by three things - he was too fat, too lazy and couldn't ride very well.

Fortunately, that's never been a barrier to a career in journalism. In fact, some might say it's obligatory.

Using his writing skills and love of racing, this quiz book has been a labour of love. Sometimes he's needed blinkers to keep the concentration levels up but the reward of seeing it in print and knowing how well the proceeds will be used by the Injured Jockeys Fund has been enough of an incentive to see it out right to the line.

Hopefully, it will be a winner with all racing fans.

ACKNOWLEDGEMENTS

The authors and Bresbet, the sponsors of the book, would like to thank the following for their generous contributions:

- focusonracing.com
- Dan Abraham
- Bernard Parkin
- Gavin James
- Bryan Mathieson
- Dave Yates
- Tim Richards
- Graham Stone
- Terry Lang
- Cornelius Lysaght
- Draper Media
- iPlus Group
- All the racing personalities who have contributed a round of questions.

THE BRESBET FOUNDATION is a not-for-profit organisation supporting a host of charities including the Injured Jockeys Fund, Racing Welfare and Greyhound Trust.

The BresBet Foundation also supports mental health and children's charities, as well as other horse and greyhound welfare-oriented organisations in addition to the IJF and GT. It will work closely with its friends at Ravenswell Farm, home of trainer Fergal O'Brien, and in particular Paddy Brennan, number one jockey at the Cotswold stables and a BresBet Legend.

Providing wide-ranging help, assistance and opportunities for all the charities it supports, the BresBet Foundation has a special connection with young Kian Burley, a hugely popular figure on the racecourse and at Ravenswell Farm.

Cerebral palsy sufferer Kian is a well-known and passionate racing fan. He has an infectious enthusiasm for life and the sport he adores and proudly wears the moniker of assistant trainer at Ravenswell Farm - with Fergal's blessing!

The BresBet Foundation will be hosting a variety of special fundraising events for all its associated charities and will work in partnership with horse racing and the wider betting industry.

BresBet Foundation trustee Becky Brereton said: "Supporting several charitable trusts is at the heart of what the BresBet Foundation is all about.

"We have assembled a fantastic group of founding trustees with the necessary skillsets to make a real difference. It involved lots of hard work to establish but we are proud of what we've done already and will be able to do in the future.

"And it's wonderful to support Kian who is an inspiration to us all, but especially to those at Ravenswell Farm. They know when Kian is around the stables you're never too far from a cheeky quip, he takes no prisoners and everyone knows where they stand. He is the boss!"

BRESBET.COM